OF PREDATION AND LIFE

PAUL L. ERRINGTON was internationally recognized for his work in the population phenomena of vertebrates, especially fur and game species, and made extensive studies in this field in North America and Northern Europe. Dr. Errington was professor of zoology at Iowa State University before his death in 1962. He became a staff member at Iowa State in 1932, the same year he received his doctorate from the University of Wisconsin. Recipient of many awards, he was given the American Wildlife Conference Aldo Leopold Medal (1962), a yearly award in recognition of the highest achievement and service to wildlife conservation. He was twice honored by the Wildlife Society for outstanding wildlife publication.

He was author of more than two hundred technical and popular articles and, besides this book, was author of *Of Men and Marshes, Muskrats and Marsh Management,* and *Muskrat Populations.*

In 1958–1959, Dr. Errington conducted research in Europe on population dynamics of higher vertebrates with the support of the Guggenheim and the National Science foundations and the Swedish government.

He was fellow of the American Association for the Advancement of Science and the American Ornithologists Union, and member of the American Society of Zoologists and numerous other scientific organizations.

Illustrated by Dycie Madson

OF PREDATION AND LIFE

PAUL L. ERRINGTON

IOWA STATE UNIVERSITY PRESS/Ames, Iowa

Composed and printed by
The Iowa State University Press

FIRST EDITION, 1967

Library of Congress Catalog Card Number: 67–20153

PREFACE

To a biologist the concept of Death being a part of Life may seem logical enough. Predation, a way of Life resulting in the death of animals preyed upon, is about as logical a consequence of Life's faculty for exploiting Life as anything that happens in the natural relationships of living things.

Predation is indeed a logical phenomenon for a biologist to be interested in but I am willing to go further than that. To me, predation can be so closely identified with the dramatic aspects of Life as to be one of the most fascinating subjects I can think of, reflecting as it does Life's adjustments and evolution under all kinds of circumstances.

I must have been about four years old when I first learned that there was such a thing as predation, the preying of one animal upon another. At that time, which was early in the century, adults could still talk at the supper table about the wolves that depredated upon the livestock of the east-central South Dakota of my birth and upbringing. At that time also I acquired my first misconception concerning predation in the fear that I personally was in great danger from the wolves, even from wolves that might come into the house after me.

The first predation victim I recall having seen was a

sheep with its side eaten away, probably by a coyote. This sight was not altogether conducive to realism in an imaginative small boy's philosophy.

I did not feel that I would ever want to go out alone in the countryside.

THEN, FROM MY earliest teens through my mid-twenties I acquired predatory skills myself as a professional hunter and fur trapper. I did this partly as apprenticeship for the naturalist's career toward which I had been aiming since childhood, partly because I loved the life of a hunter and trapper and partly because I could thereby finance my intermittent attendance at South Dakota State College, 1924–29. The game that I ate and the muskrats, minks, weasels, skunks, and coyotes that I skinned made possible some things that might not have been possible otherwise.

My early apprenticeship was invaluable to me. The hunting, trapping, and outdoor experience proved to be the best of groundwork for biological field studies. Scarcely any of my field-study techniques are without some foundation in outdoor skills developed as a youth and young man. These highly useful skills were notably in "reading of sign"—that interpretation of tracks, food remains, and a great variety of traces of animal activities.

I must acknowledge that I did have to unlearn much that I learned wrong as a hunter and trapper. My earlier tendency was to ascribe undue significance to what I could learn merely through being an outdoorsman and it took me a long time to appreciate the importance of slowly and patiently gathering facts from which to draw conclusions. I liked to take intuitive shortcuts without always reserving judgment when I had no valid basis for actually knowing. After I got a better idea of what constituted scientifically acceptable evidence and gained the objectivity to put numerous early preconceptions in their proper places, some of my earlier observations were of unique supplementary value in my career as a biologist. I saw some population phenomena when I was young that I have never had an opportunity to see since.

In comparing my earlier views on population phenomena with my later ones, the principal differences that I see relate to predation. Predation is easy to misappraise on superficial grounds and I made the usual mistakes in my early appraisals. I attributed to hawks, owls, crows, minks, weasels, wolves, coyotes, foxes, and snapping turtles predatory powers greatly exceeding any they truly possess. As I gradually learned more and more about living requirements of wild animals I came to know that animals, whether predators or prey, could not be expected to live where they did not belong. Even so, I continued to overestimate the role of predatory enemies in keeping down the numbers of familiar game or fur species, or the numbers of rats and mice about buildings, or food fishes in the lakes, or songbirds, or jackrabbits, or insect pests.

Long before I ever acquired such expressions as "territorial behavior," "biological surpluses," and "marginal environment," I felt I had answers to complex biological problems comfortably down pat. To learn what was keeping a wild population down, I was sure that all one had to do was to learn what preyed upon it.

IT WAS WHILE I was a graduate student at the University of Wisconsin, 1929–32, that my interest in predation began to grow into a scientific specialty. My Ph.D. thesis research on the bobwhite quail called for detailed work on the food habits of possible predatory enemies of the quail and appraisals of local situations involving predation.

After receiving my degree at the University of Wisconsin, I continued studying the bobwhite for many years but made muskrats and minks my principal study animals almost throughout the following thirty years as a member of the faculty of Iowa State University. Also at Iowa State I carried on long-term intensive studies of great horned owls and red foxes, together with lesser studies of barred owls, marsh hawks, and redtailed hawks, of pheasants and ducks, and of other wild species that eat flesh or are themselves eaten.

THE FILES of field notes in my office have settings that include the north-central and northwestern regions of the United States, the Prairie Provinces of Canada, the Ontario "bush," northern Denmark, southern Finland, and nearly the whole of the Scandinavian Peninsula. The settings include lands that have been under cultivation for a thousand years and some spots where conceivably I might have been the only human being ever there. They include city back yards and gardens, cornfields, pastures, weed patches, dumps, deep woods, cutover lands, big and little streams, lakes, marshes, swamps, bogs, archipelagoes, shallow seas, rocky coasts, high plains, tundras, plateaus, mountains. The settings have their storms and floods and droughts, their strong winds and deep snows and low temperatures; they have Nature in late-summer cornucopian lushness, when Life can afford to be as lavish and easy and lazy and mellow as it ever can.

As a result of my academic position at Iowa State University, it was in Iowa's prairie and partly wooded and marshy terrain that my field studies of predators and prey were chiefly carried on. Predators and prey were studied when one or the other or both were abundant or scarce; they lived their own lives on my study areas and thrived or did not thrive, in wet and dry years, cool and hot summers, mild and cold winters. Whatever happened relating to the fortunes of these animals, I tried to find out about it—especially as related to the population changes and the conditions under which the predators were able to make their kills or the prey animals were able to escape. Except in connection with planned experiments or obtaining needed specimens, I rarely interfered with any natural events.

IN MODERN BIOLOGICAL SCIENCES, of course no one person's work should stand alone. I know that my present conclusions as to predator-prey relationships are a resultant of the work of other people over the world as well as my own. I do not think that I could possibly even list the people to whom I am indebted for their contributions to my scientific development.

The one person to whom I feel most indebted, if only for reasons of a friendly and comprehensive correspondence, is the late W. L. McAtee. If I were to name a half dozen more people who deserve the most special of acknowledgments from the standpoint of my maturing philosophy on predation, they would be Frederick and Frances Hamerstrom, A. Starker Leopold, W. E. Ricker, Thomas G. Scott, and Herbert L. Stoddard. If I were to go on I could put down names by the hundreds and these would include the names of colleagues, people I have talked with at meetings, and many biologists whom I have never met but know from publications and correspondence. They would include the names of Indian trappers, commercial fishermen, lay outdoorsmen, and Old World foresters and game keepers.

THE STUDY OF PREDATION is no field for snap judgments. Cause-and-effect relationships have, on occasion, their own ways of turning out to be quite different from what they may seem to be at first. The rules of order behind Life and Life's processes hold for both predators and their prey, and the fact that these rules are not always apparent is no argument against their validity.

In following evidence on complex predator-prey relationships in the past, I have modified or even reversed certain of my previous conclusions and it is possible that I may do so again in the future. That is the prerogative of a scientist: an investigator's knowledge should be regarded as only relative.

I should be pleased to have the reader read carefully what I write, to weigh my stated conclusions against available facts, and to arrive at his own versions of truth on the basis of the evidence. In this book, I shall try as much as I can to help him do so.

PAUL L. ERRINGTON

Fall, 1962

AT THE TIME of Paul Errington's death, November 5, 1962, the manuscript of this book was in first draft. A careful revision was needed to make it ready for publication. Insofar as I had been working on the manuscript as typist and critic and knew what changes were intended, I undertook the work of revision. After the manuscript was, in my opinion, ready for publication, Dr. Milton Weller and Dr. Ira N. Gabrielson read it critically and gave me advice and assurance. To them I am indeed grateful.

CAROLYN ERRINGTON

Spring, 1967

CONTENTS

PART ONE: PRELIMINARIES

AND PERSPECTIVES

COOPER'S HAWK AND DOVES

1

GENERAL PROCEDURES:
WHAT IS ELEMENTARY
AND WHAT IS NOT

IN STUDYING PREDATOR-PREY relationships, only occasionally may the act of predation be witnessed—that dramatic
climax of seeking and pursuing. More usually, a research
worker must find evidence in stomach contents, pellets
(castings), droppings, prey remnants, and field observations. Each source of evidence has its values and its
limitations.

Stomach contents have a reassuring definiteness about
them. We always know that the predator ate the stuff,
however little we may know about the circumstances of
the eating. Balanced against the Q.E.D. finality of a stomach's identity is another sort of finality—that last meal may
conclude one's opportunity for learning about the food
habits of that particular predator. That is all. It is fin-
ished. There will not be any more.

I have found examination of droppings or pellets of
predatory mammals and birds as useful as any single technique in the study of food habits. They may often be obtained in large quantities, as a more or less continuing
record of what certain individual predators or groups of
predators may be eating. That they also have their technical disadvantages soon becomes apparent to anyone
working with them.

The people I know who collect pellets or droppings

as part of their food habits work are now and then confronted by troublesome or impossible problems of identification. I have known what it is to discard entire lots of pellets or droppings for the simple reason that they contained too much matter of uncertain origin.

On the whole, the best collections come from latrines of minks or foxes or raccoons, or from roosting sites of birds of prey, or from other places that tend to be used for varying periods with some exclusiveness by known species of predators. In addition to using latrines, minks may deposit their droppings on logs or rocks, along trails, and on or about muskrat lodges; foxes, at scent stations or next to carrion, along trails, and on or about muskrat lodges; and raccoons, on fallen trees, along trails, and on the butts of old muskrat lodges. When trails or muskrat lodges are used in common by the minks, foxes, and raccoons as deposition sites for droppings, the droppings from these species are usually readily distinguishable by size and appearance. The mink is weasellike; the fox, doglike; and the reference to the raccoon as little brother to the bear is not wholly misleading with regard to its droppings. Horned and barred owls may have their strategic retreats in wood lots, barn owls in quarries or steeples, longeared owls in evergreen plantings and willow thickets. Cemeteries are often good places to find owl pellets and, with practice, an investigator can learn a great deal about the range of other possibilities.

Of all the pellets and droppings with which I have worked, I have found owl pellets most satisfactory for analysis. These may be spread out on a flat surface so that teeth, characteristic bones, feathers, tufts of fur, etc., may easily be looked at; skulls, feet, shoulder and pelvic girdles, and ends of bones are usually worth more careful scrutiny and serve well for comparison with specimens in a reference collection. The bony contents of hawk pellets may be badly digested compared with those of owl pellets, but the resistant hair, feathers, horny parts of beaks or feet, fish scales, and insect chitin may show up well.

Examination of mammal droppings may call for more

care and skill than examination of pellets of birds of prey. Bones in droppings tend to be broken up and eroded, and fur and feather material may need washing through a strainer to free it from gummy or claylike waste. Fox droppings, in particular, may need washing and then drying before examination. Droppings have further shortcomings in that food residues may be held in a carnivore stomach for a few days (or up to a week or longer) before a little pinch of fur or feathers dribbles through into the intestine to be passed.

When considered alone, fragments of prey at feeding places or partly eaten carcasses may have their deficiencies, even when no doubt exists as to the identity of the animals doing the eating. Remains of a fox-eaten pheasant may be conspicuously in sight for weeks or months, whereas the mice, gulped down as staple prey, may seldom show at feeding places of the foxes except possibly as a blood drop or a wisp of loose fur on the snow.

It is evident that the fullest combination of methods may be needed to give a truer, more representative picture of what a predator eats. Then there may be the problem of judging how much of the food was carrion, and, if recognizable carrion, how much represents what the predator found dead or killed at an earlier date.

GRADUALLY, AS MY earlier studies of predation went on, it became clear that to understand predation it was necessary to understand prey populations.

Studies of populations may lead into the mysteries of soils, of weather, of "cyclic" changes in physiology and psychology of animals, and of the trial-and-error adjustments that animals have evolved in living together over long periods of time. The fossil and historical records demonstrate that animal populations are not always successful in making adjustments; that predators as well as prey can become much reduced or extinct over the earth. Yet animals can spread and increase with remarkable rapidity or maintain themselves for years without pronounced changes in their population levels.

Long-term data are especially valuable in helping to provide the perspective needed to distinguish between what counts more and what counts less in complex situations. Conclusions based upon less comprehensive data may be shaky to the point of being misleading. Mortality may be heavy, but if occurring under conditions favoring natural compensation, it may have little or no real influence on the population levels maintained by the prey species concerned. Or, mortality may be rather light in terms of numbers or percentages of prey animals dying and still have disproportionally severe population effects if suffered by populations having little or no resilience.

Conformity or lack of conformity to patterns may provide some of the best evidence as to population effects of predation. If the year-by-year trend of a prey population follows a definite population curve or a similar mathematical pattern for a number of years, irrespective of wide differences in the predation actually suffered by the prey, then it would seem that something other than the predation must be the true regulating factor. Predators may be varied and abundant in a given area, and still a prey population may maintain itself without so much as a kink in its population curve, with no more depression in the curve when the predators are abundant than when they are scarce.

But when a kink in the curve does occur, it is not always clear what factor is the influential one, predation or something else. It is still necessary to consider many kinds of evidence to learn more precisely how predation fits into the picture.

2

PREDATION AS A
WAY OF LIFE

PREDATION IS A natural form of exploitation of one living
thing by another, engaged in by the widest variety of
animal life. For purposes of this book it is the killing and
eating of one animal by another, and I shall not attempt
refining definitions to allow for all possible variations or
exceptions. The reader of the following chapters will, I
am sure, recognize what is meant by predation when he
reads about it.

Unfortunately, the expression "predatory animal"
arouses in many people disdain, hatred, and condemnation
of predators on moral grounds. Except for civilized man's
participation in predatory activities, I do not see that predation is anything to be judged by human moral standards at all. As a way of life it reflects adaptations of animals for living and it is the only way that countless species
of animals can live. It is a resultant of adaptations and opportunities, of physiology and psychology, of experience,
and of heredity and racial history. I can conceive of a
friendly lion and a trusting lamb lying down together as
companions, for odd associations occur from time to time
on an individual basis. However, such a lion, to keep
functional as a living lion, would have to satisfy the nutritional requirements of its body by eating some other lamb
or some other suitable protein food.

9

LAND OTTER

I think that I understand the psychological reaction of many people to sights of messy predation—I have seen plenty that I did not enjoy seeing. If a robin pulls an earthworm in two most of us think nothing of it, and I doubt that many people feel much sympathy for the mouse caught by a cat. But when something big is killed and left partly eaten, there is more of blood and guts and hide and bones and head and feet to impress our consciousness. If by chance the big victim has been eaten upon and is not even dead, we are apt to project ourselves into the place of the victim, and then it is especially hard to be objective. When seeing a movie of a steer being eaten alive by piranhas in a Brazilian river, I became aware of a feeling of revulsion, despite my years of scientific work on predation, and I thought how easily a person might see in such an event unnatural evil that was not there.

There is little in non-human predation that is deliberately cruel. What we call cruelty in these relationships is far more likely to be a manifestation of behavior that is unimaginative and matter-of-fact; of animals living their own lives in their own ways.

WEASELS ARE TRADITIONALLY regarded as bloodthirsty scourges of forest and meadow. They may take conspicuous advantage of available types of prey that they can easily handle—from chickens in a coop to mice in a straw stack—and may work themselves to exhaustion killing and carrying and heaping up victims if the victims are available. The epithet "bloodthirsty" connotes something that seldom seems to be literally true, and wholesale killing of prey by weasels should be thought of more as a response to a stimulus. As a usual thing, our north-central weasels do not have unlimited opportunities for killing. The smaller weasels may feed heavily upon insects, and so may the larger when insects such as beetles and grasshoppers are especially available. Mice, fledgling small birds, young cottontails, and ground squirrels constitute rather typical weasel prey, and the victims of the larger weasels may include some as large as full-grown snowshoe hares. Some of the larger prey animals may be dangerous for weasels to attack, however, and there are published accounts of cottontail rabbits fatally injuring weasels that were experimentally put in cages with them.

In its hunting, a weasel does much exploring of holes, much bounding back and forth in such places as meadows and hayfields, stream and marsh edges, weed patches, dumps, wood lots. I have been impressed by the noisiness of a weasel's hunting in dry vegetation as it bounded amid leaves and rushes and weeds. A weasel may be either bold or circumspect in the presence of man or some other potential enemy, and the frequency with which weasels are killed by foxes and horned owls is proof that, for all of their agility and fighting prowess, weasels can make serious mistakes. Sometimes the losses that they suffer look severe and out of all proportion to their relative abundance in an area.

Concerning other members of the weasel family: Land otters are expert at catching fishes but they may subsist largely upon frogs or crayfishes, or they may prey upon conveniently available mammals and birds. Badgers may dig out mice or ground squirrels, raid bee or hornet nests, and eat bird eggs, snakes, frogs, beetles, grasshoppers, and crickets. The agile little spotted skunks include in their diets more prey of types taken by weasels—rats about buildings, mice, rabbits, birds as opportunities permit, and the beetles and grasshoppers that may become abundant and available at certain times and places. Striped skunks, being far more sluggish than the spotted skunks, usually take less of mammal and bird prey (except for eggs of ground-nesting birds where these are highly available) and more of insects, especially the grasshoppers and crickets that may be so abundant on the north-central prairies when striped skunks are storing fat for hibernation.

Members of the weasel family do not, as a rule, eat much of plant foods, though there can be exceptions. Spotted skunks may eat ear corn, and certain highly predacious forms such as the pine marten may eat large quantities of fruits. European badgers include much plant matter in their diets.

Omnivorous habits are indeed characteristic of many mammals that are labeled carnivorous. It seems almost unnecessary to mention that the same bears that are legendary lovers of fruits and honey may also feed upon ground squirrels, fishes, marmots, and big game and domestic stock when they have good chances. Iowa raccoons may make a virtually straight diet of corn and wild fruits for weeks or months, or there may be hardly anything in their diets except crayfishes. Prey species that can move enough to keep out of reach of bears and raccoons will be eaten mainly as they are caught at some disadvantage or found dead.

Really adept predators such as red foxes and coyotes may all but go off a meat standard in their feeding at times when some especially relished plant material is abundantly available to them. In parts of western United States, coyotes may become a nuisance not because of their depredations upon poultry or livestock but because of their appetite for melons. North-central red foxes may gorge upon corn in roasting ear stages or feed upon fruits almost to the extent that raccoons do. But the coyotes and foxes have more leeway in their responses to what may come their way as vulnerable prey. Let a surplus of rabbits, ground squirrels, mice, bird life, or large relished insects appear, and the foxes and coyotes can be counted upon to take advantage of the most attractive opportunities.

Among the common hawks and owls of north-central United States, we find examples of predatory behavior that can be either stereotyped or opportunistic, or, more likely, showing combinations of both. Local barn owls may subsist almost entirely upon mice and shrews, then starve to death in the midst of an abundant population of small birds as deepening snows give the mice and shrews increased protection. Longeared or shorteared owls may winter by the dozens in willow thickets and feed upon almost nothing but mice, yet these owls living where a wide choice of other prey is available for the taking may also feed upon small birds, birds the size of quail, and even the formidable barn rats. During the summer months when prey resources are more varied than in winter, the longears and shortears may take advantage of large insects about the same as do other predatory creatures that take what they can get.

Burrowing owls eat their mice, ground squirrels, small birds, frogs, and large insects much according to relative availability. The most versatile feeders among our small- and medium-sized north-central owls are the screech owls, in build and temperament like miniature horned owls. Screech owls take their mice and shrews and small birds as a matter of course. They may occasionally take something like a domestic pigeon that must give them a real tussle, despite the power in the little screech owl feet. At the right times of year, they turn readily to May beetles and other insects, quite as one might expect.

The Swainson's hawks of the semi-arid western part of the north-central region feed upon mice and ground squirrels, snakes, young rabbits, and the more catchable young birds. Sometimes, they feed upon grasshoppers in

COYOTE AND MELONS

tremendous numbers. Others in this soaring-hawk group include the American roughlegged hawks, which are winter visitors from the northern tundras. They prey mainly upon mice because mice are mostly what their hunting adaptations permit them to catch in our winter out-of-doors. On the other hand, redtailed hawks may be able to surprise and capture a considerable variety of prey besides their staple mice and ground squirrels. Rabbits, fox squirrels, poultry, and medium-sized birds are prey items requiring, if nothing else, more strength to handle than mice and ground squirrels.

In studies of food habits of all of these large, relatively slow, soaring hawks, it is often difficult or impossible to distinguish between hawk-killed prey and already dead material obtained by scavenging. They all scavenge when they have attractive opportunities as upon animal life killed on highways by motor traffic. I have seen a group of redtails feeding upon the fresh carcass of another redtail that itself had been struck by an automobile.

The more agile and swift-flying blue-darter hawks of wooded places differ more in size and strength than in hunting methods. In north-central United States, the principal representatives of this group are the Cooper's hawks, which live largely upon common birds of small–medium sizes, such as flickers and other woodpeckers, mourning doves, meadowlarks, robins, quail, young pheasants, young chickens, and bluejays. They may also take birds of sparrow and warbler sizes. Although they are real "bird hawks," Cooper's hawks may respond to special availability of prey species as different as fishes and ground squirrels. Their smaller relatives, the sharpshinned hawks, are usually seen rather briefly in the north-central region during spring and fall migration; they feed upon warblers, sparrows, and similar birds. The diets of goshawks—the largest members of the blue-darter group—run more to larger prey. During the occasional winter when goshawks move southward from their northern wilderness range, their depredations upon wintering ducks, grouse, quail, and pheasants may be conspicuous, but smaller birds may still make up much of their diet; hares and rabbits may be staple foods when available.

Blue-darter hawks may or may not be persistent in their attacks. At times they may make an unsuccessful pass at an intended victim, then fly off out of the neighborhood. At other times they may perch for hours, waiting for hiding birds to show themselves again. Or they may pursue birds on foot through briar thickets or under brush piles.

Falcons comprise another group of mainly bird-eating hawks. Unlike the blue-darters—which have short, rounded wings adapted for sprint flying and tails that serve as effective rudders in quick turns—the falcons have long, pointed wings primarily adapted for sustained speed through open air. The rare peregrine falcons that breed in North America are known as duck hawks, and, while they are capable of overtaking and killing ducks, their usual prey in our north-central region consists of domestic pigeons and land birds of similar or smaller sizes. The near relatives of the peregrines, the prairie falcons of the western states, may either overtake birds in the air or prey heavily upon rabbits and ground squirrels. Prairie falcons may also gorge on grasshoppers.

Our real grasshopper hawks during the grasshopper season are the so-called sparrow hawks, the smallest North American hawks. These are true falcons, having the typical falcon build, but they have a manner of hunting that shows little of the dash of the larger falcons. Sparrow hawks like to sit on dead stumps or on telephone poles. While hunting they often hover by means of rapidly beating wings over a particular spot in a field. During cold weather they feed upon such mice and small birds as they can catch and handle, much the sort of prey that screech owls take.

The fish-feeding ospreys have, in their powerful talons, the physical equipment to kill other prey, and sometimes they do kill land animals; but in general their preying is sharply restricted by the psychological peculiarities of the ospreys themselves.

When we consider predation by birds other than hawks and owls we find that killing and feeding conforms to much the same patterns of adaptation and availability. Shrikes (called butcher birds) lack effective talons but do have raptorial beaks, and they can impale the bodies of mice, small birds, and large insects on thorns, or on barbed wire fences, and then tear off pieces to eat. Large herons feed upon fishes, frogs, and snakes—also upon mice, ground squirrels, pocket gophers, and large insects, including grasshoppers. Mergansers are called fish ducks, and their sawtooth beaks are adapted to hold slippery small fishes, but they may frequent fishless waters and feed upon little except water insects. Gulls and crows may either scavenge or prey upon helpless living things that they find in sufficient abundance to attract them—the large insects, bird eggs, waterfowl sickening because of botulism—just about whatever there may be that is suitable for exploitation.

Opportunistic aspects of predation may be noted not only when the land swarms with eligible prey—be it mice, rabbits, or grasshoppers—but also when emergencies concentrate or evict substantial parts of prey populations. The last fish-filled puddles of a drying stream bed have their raccoons, minks, foxes, herons, kingfishers, and snakes working them. Garter snakes crisscross squirming masses of minnows, diving and pursuing. Other predators feed upon the garter snakes along with the fishes. I have watched flocks of robins walking in the watery mud of a drying pool, catching and eating the exposed minnows of manageable sizes, the same as "real" predators would be doing.

Opportunistic predators do not have to be wild animals or anything commonly thought of as predacious. Domestic chickens may eat small frogs, small snakes, and eggs of small birds along with their beetles, crickets, and grasshoppers. When pecking at the flesh of a large animal, chickens are not too particular as to whether it is dead or not quite dead, so long as it is helpless. Turkeys may take a larger size-range of occasional prey—the eggs and fledgling birds, the frogs and snakes and lizards, the snails, the mice—along with their beetles, crickets, and grasshoppers.

Pigs are known for their omnivorous propensities, and the differences between their scavenging on a carcass and preying upon sluggish or weak animal life may not be great. Pigs may work a lake shore eating the dead and ailing fishes that come drifting in. They may root crayfishes out of burrows or from under rocks; they may feed upon turtle eggs and clams; they may open accessible muskrat lodges in search of what they can find that cannot get away. They may catch snakes in a pasture or young chickens about a farmyard.

The fact that animals do not invariably behave like automatons in their preying and feeding should not recede too far from our minds when we think of flesh-eaters responding to availability of food. While the pigs, for example, might be expected to eat grasshoppers in large quantities if they found them in an inactive condition and covering the ground, I have watched enough of the feeding of pigs to judge that pigs are not going to devote much time to catching animals of such small sizes if the task becomes too bothersome. Nor does it follow, when any one species of prey animal is highly available and suitable for food, that every predator that can eat it will invariably do so. Alaskan lynxes have been known to starve during a winter of scarcity of snowshoe hares, their staple food, despite the continued abundance of mice, though the occasional lynx that learned to hunt mice grew fat.

IT IS INDEED EASY to visualize man as having been primarily a hunter or fisherman back in the millennia of prehistory long before he ever became a herdsman or developed any sort of agricultural or manufacturing economy. We can easily visualize him prowling beaches or woodlands grabbing lesser prey with his hands or digging food animals out of mud or sand or knocking them down with sticks long before he ever fashioned real tools or weapons for hunting or any other purposes. The mere probability—to judge from his omnivore's teeth if nothing else—that he supplemented his flesh eating with plant foods does not detract from the fact that man has a lot of predatory exploitation of animal life in his background.

During historical times there have been (and still are, for that matter) hunting and fishing cultures, sometimes combined with pastoral or agricultural or industrial cultures, sometimes not. The first white plainsmen in North America found whole Indian nations dependent upon bison hunting; and the predatory skills of American pioneers have become legendary. Whoever thinks of Daniel Boone as subsisting on food other than the game he took with his rifle? Even the modern sportsman, in his increasingly ritualistic hunting and fishing, justifies his sport at least partly in terms of reliving—after a fashion—some of his racial past.

In its elementary aspects, a great deal of human predation follows the same rules of order that other predation may be expected to follow. Often the parts of prey populations that are most conspicuous and easiest for both human and non-human predators to take are the individuals that are available chiefly for the reason that they live in the less suitable grades of their environment, or are present in greater numbers than their environment can securely accommodate.

I remember how my own predation of many years ago could show in its broader outlines a striking dependence upon simple availability of prey. Neither I nor my fellow predators, the minks, would have much success in preying upon any of the thousands of sound, never-taking-chances mallards that sat in the center of a lake by day and fed in distant cornfields by night; but we did prey upon the less wary or shot-pricked or otherwise somewhat handicapped birds that might be living more vulnerably in the reedy shore zones. Similarly, the foxes, the large hawks, and I took advantage of the relatively few though easily obtainable cottontail rabbits that tried to winter in open fields and pastures—too far away from the brushy undergrowth and thickets where rabbits lived in both greater numbers and greater security. One summer I shared with a bear the prowling ground afforded by a Montana creek valley. The ripe berries, which could not get away from either of us, we both ate; but neither of us ate the half-dozen big trout, veterans in the testing for survival, that wheeled like an infantry squad to disappear in the protecting depths of a beaver burrow at the first suggestion of movement near the edge of the dam pond.

Predation by modern man can of course differ in degree and specialization from that exerted by non-human animals. The nets, traps, snares, radar apparatus, motor vehicles, improved firearms and ammunition, and all of the mechanical gadgets that man uses to aid him in exploiting animal life may allow him advantages far exceeding the natural advantages of even the most biologically gifted of wild predators. When we think even of the superb adaptations of a peregrine falcon for its own predatory life, or the adaptations of a goshawk, an otter, a wolf, a killer whale, or virtually any animal possessed only of its own natural weapons and means of pursuit, we can see that man patently belongs in a unique predatory category. The specialness of human predation becomes further apparent when we think of the categories of prey that man exploits: anything from his captive livestock that he butchers when he pleases, to staple food fishes, sport-hunted game, and rare fur bearers threatened by extinction.

And, if we consider the pressure man may exert on wild populations when he kills merely to get rid of such animals as he regards as troublesome, we soon come to the point where further analogies between what man does and what wild predators do may become pointless.

3

PREDATION FROM
THE STANDPOINT OF
THE PREDATORS

WHENEVER MOST OF US witness an attack by a predator upon some prospective prey animal, our sympathies are usually with the prey unless it is a despised form such as a barn rat, or is something we ourselves are interested in preying upon and which the predator (such as a hound or bird dog) is helping us to obtain. When we intervene in behalf of the prey—the hawk flies off screaming while the rabbit escapes scared though not seriously injured—we can feel complacent.

We—that is, we collectively—can feel this way even when we have no real animosity toward predators nor any fault to find, in the abstract, with the overall phenomenon of predation. For, after all, even when the encounter may not be particularly violent nor distasteful to watch, there is something in the respective stakes involved for the predator and the prey to throw human sympathies on the side of the prey. If it turns out one way an animal loses its life; the other way the predator loses only a meal.

In the cartoons the wolf can go home and open a can of beans after its designs against pigs have been thwarted, and that humorous and fanciful thought is quite as it should be—in cartoons. In real life we are justified in thwarting predatory attacks upon our poultry or livestock. I would say that we also have the right to protect, if we do

21

it in a responsible manner, certain individuals or species of wild animals that we particularly wish to protect. But I cannot see that we are justified in going out of our way to thwart, irrespective of circumstances, every predatory attack that we may ever see upon a rabbit, robin, mourning dove, meadowlark, deer, or other common form of wildlife. When it comes to justifying such interference as a matter of civilized ethics, I cannot agree at all.

It may be claimed that predators are gluttonous. The abdominal bulges of foxes, the distended crops of hawks, and the filled-up owls with long feathers or tails sticking out of their mouths can be thought of as supporting that idea. "Gluttony" is not a word that man ordinarily uses in a complimentary sense. My contention is that if we are to understand predation realistically, we can better do so by regarding wild animals as wild animals, whether flesh eaters or plant eaters, and not judge them by human standards.

The physiology of predacious species may allow more irregularity in their feeding than may the physiology of plant eaters, though this is not always true. Shrews, with their high metabolic rate, must eat relatively great quantities of the small animals that constitute their diet or they die. Some of the small insect-eating birds may not need to spend so much of each twenty-four hours eating as do the shrews but they do have to keep busy at it to live. At other extremes are slow-living reptiles that require only a meal in months.

The predatory species that have been my specialties over the years are all adapted to do some fasting when necessary. They are adapted to endure the hungriness of youth when they are learning to be self-sufficient and find food hard to get. They can "sit out" moderate spells of bad weather, even during periods of decided undernourishment, and still maintain their strength and predatory faculties fairly well. Part of their adaptation for a predacious life is an ability to make up for their fasts, to be good stuffers when they do get access to an abundance of food.

LET US CONSIDER predation from the standpoint of the mink. The mink is a "real pro" among our native predators, a good "general practitioner." It can climb, range overland by the mile, swim and dive expertly, enter rather small holes, dig and bite its way through rather hard ground or into icy muskrat lodges, and it is proficient at locating either prey or edible carrion by smell. It is a quick-moving and well-coordinated animal having stamina and great strength and physical toughness for its size.

I remember, from experiences of my fur-trapping years, how much I was impressed by the ability of minks to take punishment. I usually examined the bodies of my trapped minks with some thoroughness, and six of the nineteen Big Sioux River minks on which I kept notes had healed shot wounds. These were all minks that had lived along stretches of brush-bordered river much frequented by rabbit hunters, and I knew of several attempts by hunters to shoot minks that they had encountered. Of the six minks with healed shot wounds, three had been so badly wounded that I would not have expected them to recover. However, not one of them had been handicapped in any way that I could see at the time of capture. One, a female struck broadside by about fifteen shot of number five or six size, had punctures about an inch and a half apart, well-healed but betrayed by the pulled-in tufts of fur. Another, a male, had healed wounds on head and neck suggesting that while peering out of a hole it had taken a shot charge at a distance of about thirty-five feet from a choke-bored, twelve-gauge shotgun. The other of the three badly wounded minks, another male, had taken on its rump a closely-massed charge of number five shot, some of which had passed through its body from the rear to lodge in the abdominal wall.

The mink has an ability to get along on a meager diet if it must, and recorded differences in daily food consumption of minks living about Iowa marshes illustrate the nutritional resilience of the species under natural conditions. During one spring period of convenient availability of muskrat prey, a big mink ate an average of two adult-sized muskrats per day, gorging to the extent that at times its droppings consisted of undigested meat. Ordinarily, on a straight diet of muskrats in spring, a big mink would probably be eating an adult-sized muskrat every other day. But a muskrat every other day far exceeds the minimum of flesh required for a subsistence diet. Very careful studies indicated that the minks of a central Iowa marsh were maintaining themselves in normal health for about half of one winter on as little food as the straight-diet equivalent of one muskrat per nine days.

For still another reason, a mink is unlikely to find itself desperate for food in its usual north-central environment. When hungry it is not very particular as to what it eats so long as the food is animal protein.

The closeness with which minks may scavenge is exemplified by the contents of some of the cold-season droppings to be found about north-central lakes and marshes, by tail and foot bones of muskrats, butts of wing- or tail-feathers, coarse material mixed with mud. I have known a free-living wild mink to eat in a couple of days most of the body of a muskrat liquifying from decay. Hence, the food supply has to be short indeed to impose a desperate hunger crisis upon a species that can be adept at either scavenging or hunting.

In its strictly predatory activities, the mink can attack savagely or it can withdraw if it sees ahead more trouble than it wants at the time. Just because it can put up a terrific fight is no reason why it should choose to do so each time that it wants to eat.

Undoubtedly, muskrat flesh is one of the mink's favorite foods. Undoubtedly also, the mink is one of the most accomplished killers of muskrats among the wild predators frequenting north-central marshes and streams. Once a large mink succeeds in grappling a muskrat, that muskrat has little chance of escaping. (In grappling, a mink hugs the victim with forelegs while it scratches violently with hind legs and bites vital parts, especially about head and neck.)

However, even a large mink diligently seeking opportunities to kill muskrats may not find it easy to follow through its muskrat hunting to grappling stages. It just about needs to find its prospective muskrat victim handicapped by some kind of trouble—some muskrat-between-muskrat hostility or some weather or hunger or eviction emergency that puts muskrats on ice or dry land. The young muskrats that take refuge in the inviting mink trails of the shore zone of a marsh, the strife-battered transient muskrats that sit around shore, the muskrats of almost any age, size, or sex that must leave their safer retreats to range in dangerous places are among those encountered and killed by minks.

The mink, which does not have anywhere nearly the expertness of the muskrat as a swimmer or diver, apparently even avoids encounters with at least the larger muskrats in the water. Several people have, to my knowledge, observed minks being driven out of the water by aggressive muskrats. Although muskrats customarily leave a lodge when a mink invades it, they can be savage defenders when the lodge is of special importance to them—as when it contains a litter of suckling young or when the occupants have no other suitable place of refuge. It is often clear from the way that undoubtedly formidable minks avoid digging into certain lodges, that those minks have a fair idea of what can be dangerous for them.

Nor is the mink's mastery of a marsh and its muskrats necessarily complete at times of drought exposure, freeze-out, or other natural crises that deprive muskrats of the defensive advantage of water. Often, a big muskrat may live on a dry marsh for weeks, right in the midst of the thoroughly worked hunting grounds of many minks. I have seen in snow where a big mink started to enter a shallow hole containing a big muskrat—and backed out again. I have "read sign" of numerous encounters of minks and muskrats on the frozen surface of marshes on which desperate muskrats were foraging. Most of the resulting kills were of muskrats that panicked and tried to escape the minks by running, and which the minks then overtook, seized by neck or shoulder, and grappled, thresh-

ing over the ice or snow. On the other hand, really functional muskrats that carried the fight to the minks seemed
to stand a fair chance.

It is not that a mink usually could not kill a muskrat
under such circumstances. If they fought to a finish, I
suppose that any ordinary mink could kill any muskrat of
equal weight; but, bite for bite, a fighting muskrat can cut
through about as much thick hide and flesh and tendon
as a mink can.

Minks and muskrats may at times occupy different parts
of the same burrow system or lodge without either species
manifesting recognizable neuroses. From the close prox-
imity in which they then live, I would judge that a
certain wary toleration of each other exists and that the
muskrats do not regard those particular minks as being
sufficiently dangerous to become very excited about. The
more I think of it, the more it seems to me that mink predation upon muskrats tends to be almost restricted to those
individuals or parts of a muskrat population that may
properly be referred to as the push-overs.

About 70 per cent of the muskrat food of central Iowa
minks has proved to represent scavenging upon victims of
disease or climatic emergencies. The minks thus got a
substantial amount of muskrat flesh without fighting for it.
Sometimes this was the case for weeks at a stretch when
much dying of muskrats was in progress. Similar scavenging upon the ducks that die from gunshot wounds or
lead poisoning is to be expected when minks hunt on shot-
over marshes. On some Iowa marshes the bodies of hundreds of hunter-killed coots may be available to scavengers
throughout the winter months, and the minks are among
the flesh-eaters that may eat these as staple food.

During the open-water months, crayfishes are the most
generally available prey of Iowa minks. The minks get
them in wet meadows, marsh edges, oxbows, pasture
brooks, spring or tile pools, and practically all places frequented by the different kinds of crayfishes. The crayfishes may be in burrows or in mud pockets; they may be
hiding under rocks of a stream bottom; they may be swimming or crawling in the water, or clambering outside on

the banks. The minks seek them or just encounter them either in or out of the water. Sometimes, crayfishes may be present in quantities of hundreds of pounds per acre of wetlands.

Or, along a stream the minks find minnows or larger fishes in riffle pools, eddies, pools below mouths of tiles, pools under drifted debris, or in watery cavities in banks or up under tree roots. I have seen minks making short dives and coming up with fishes now and then, but they get many of their fishes in land-locked puddles or corner them somewhere, as in crayfish burrows or under drift-wood. When the minks do find a fish population that they can readily exploit, they may cache the victims in holes or heap them about landing places. The upper size limits of the fishes preyed upon by minks seem determined by what the minks can seize with their limited jaw spread and handle comfortably once they do get a hold—usually nothing more than half as heavy as the mink itself.

My impression is that the minks of my study areas seldom utilized frogs and fresh water clams quite in proportion to availability during the warm weather months, but perhaps neither the frogs nor the clams were the most convenient staple mink foods even when conspicuously abundant. Maybe the lively frogs were too much of a nuisance to catch or the clamshells too much of a nuisance to open up while the crayfishes remained such a satisfactory food item. It may be significant that frogs and clams were apt to be taken as main staples in winter, after the greater part of the crayfish retreats were ice-sealed. Although minks eat some crayfishes in winter as they find them, such as those in open water or crawling over wet ice during thaws, they plainly have less access to them then.

After a general ice-seal, the minks may have ready access to the water in only a few places. They may find places where swift current or decaying vegetation or springs prevent freezing, where there are pressure-buckled ice ridges or unfrozen spots remaining beneath snowdrifts, or open water in the vicinity of muskrat burrows or lodges. The minks may use the plunge holes of muskrats to reach water beneath thick ice even though such behavior does not necessarily afford them opportunities to exploit the muskrats. Not only may fishes congregate in the plunge holes and chambers of the muskrat burrows and lodges—particularly in response to oxygen deficiency—but the muskrat retreats also provide operational bases useful to the minks in their under-ice searching for frogs, clams, water insects, and other aquatic prey.

The responsiveness of minks to attractive sources of aquatic prey may be pronounced. When they discover a wintering pool of frogs, or a lakeside spring full of desperate fishes, the minks may pack up to hundreds of pounds of frog or fish victims in the tunnels of a single snowdrift. Mink-used shelves under ice-heaves may be left littered with empty clamshells if clams happen to be available in great quantities. The minks, however, do not eat just anything in the way of animal protein that they may have convenient access to, for they regularly discard the black egg masses of our common north-central leopard frogs. Only on one occasion do I recall ever seeing frog eggs in mink droppings.

Insofar as a mink does not have anywhere nearly the ability to swim submerged that the muskrat has, its hunting radius from a plunge hole or other opening in the ice is short unless it can frequently stick out its head to breathe. If there is an air space between the water and the lower side of the ice, as often exists along the margins of streams in midwinter, a mink can range farther away from a particular landing. In neither my trapping nor research experience have I often recognized evidence of minks swimming submerged as far as fifty feet from an ice-shelf landing or a muskrat plunge hole—though I am unable to say how much such shortness in radius of activity was due to physical necessity or to disinclinations of the minks to range out farther. The typical behavior of a mink working from an icy plunge hole seems to be to dive frequently and come back soon.

When hunting on land the mink is its own opportunistic self. It bounds along the edge of a water course or through rushes or weeds or brush or timber, sniffing at the entrances of holes or under overhanging tree roots or wherever else it may expect to find something edible that cannot get away. It catches the cottontails that do not do the right thing, the fledgling birds, the mice darting across open spaces, the frogs, garter snakes, grasshoppers and crickets, May beetles, the occasional crayfish that wanders over the higher ground. Mink droppings may contain remains of the big black and yellow garden spiders, of carrion beetles, of pocket gophers and ground squirrels, of flickers and robins and grackles and wrens and bitterns—rarely of toad. In common with almost all other north-central flesh-eaters, minks patently do not relish toads.

From my observations of hunting minks, I should say that the species has little use for a stealthy approach. A mink may move quietly in soft snow or on bare ice because of the nature of its footing, or it may slip easily through water; but in running through dry vegetation, like a weasel it too can be noisy enough to arouse doubts that it cares whether prospective prey hears it coming or not. Although such noisiness combined with violent movements should not be without utility in scaring up mice, fledglings, large insects, or something crippled or ailing—and the mink is an alert hunter—the pattern of searching adds up to a rather undiscriminating opportunism. What is edible or cannot get away or cannot protect itself will be eaten to at least a considerable degree in proportion to the opportunities that minks have for finding it by sight or by scent.

RED FOXES ARE equipped with an excellent sense of smell. Their sense of hearing is not misrepresented by their large ears, as anyone can see while watching a fox as it listens during a mouse hunt in an open field. These foxes are capable of stealthy approaches and sudden dashes, which may be terminated by a leap into the air after a flushing bird. They are alert in their demeanor, light and quick in their movements, and have biting power similar to that of a small dog. As predators they give somewhat the impression of fragility, and they simply do not have the prowess to overcome very formidable prey in a violent body-to-body struggle. Through astuteness and agility, however, they may, as an extreme case, prey upon something as formidable as an immense snapping turtle on a dry marsh bottom. The upper size limits of animals that I have known to be killed by North American foxes are exemplified by turkeys, large domestic geese, large lambs, and full-grown white-tailed jack rabbits, but I am sure that they could also take such prey as unprotected young deer if they had opportunities.

As may be judged from the reputation that red foxes have for "foxiness," their hunting aptitudes can be rather special at times. They may seek out a particular kind of prey from apparent preference; they may learn to take advantage of the behavior patterns of their favorite prey; they may appraise emergency situations affecting prey animals; they may show considerable individuality in what they do, in their preying as well as in taking care of themselves otherwise. Nevertheless, the predatory behavior of the common run of foxes shows its stereotyping, its responsiveness to the prey that is conveniently available to them.

Mice and rabbits are the usual staple food of foxes in the north-central region. At the edges of woods and marshes and out in the fields (where red foxes do most of their hunting on my study areas), these are prey animals that foxes frequently find at a disadvantage. The foxes may dig the mice out of surface nests or other flimsy cover. They may sneak up on rabbits hiding in tufts of grass or at the base of trees or in light brush, sometimes to catch them, sometimes not. Grasshoppers and May beetles may be eaten at times of seasonal abundance. Not being restricted to a protein diet, foxes may sometimes show more interest in the waste apples of an orchard than in the mice and rabbits living there. Ill-situated or crippled quail and pheasants are taken according to opportunities.

Some prey is relished, meadow mice in particular, and these may be eaten as caught and so completely that remains may not be found about dens or feeding places—only in the fox droppings. Other mice, though preyed upon, may not be especially relished by the foxes. I have seen the uneaten bodies of harvest mice left in a heap in front of a fox den at the same time that the foxes were subsisting largely on meadow mice. Weasels and moles are killed but are regarded with such distaste by the foxes that they are rarely eaten except by the very hungry.

Day-by-day hunting fortunes of the foxes may be extremely variable. Snow trails representing their unsuccessful hunts may cross marshes and plowed fields, circle straw stacks and muskrat lodges, follow roads and fence rows, lead through weed patches and thickets and wood lots, go over hills and along stream valleys. Foxes *can* starve in the more food-poor areas, but intensified searching for food by hungry foxes is directed toward edible carrion as well as toward live prey. They eat the wildlife victims of motor traffic, the game birds dead from shot wounds, the dead chickens and dead suckling pigs scattered over fields along with farm manure.

And red foxes are not improvident at times of abundance of food. They leave mice or rabbits or pheasants cached (usually more or less covered with dirt or snow) about their home ranges to return to eat of them if need be. They cache not only their own killed prey but also animal remains that they find dead. I have known them repeatedly to dig up and re-bury dead coots and dead ducks from a shot-over marsh. They may even dig down through many feet of snowdrift after this material and use it for scent stations as well as for emergency food.

(The foxes show another tendency in their treatment of frozen carrion—to bite off and swallow such extremities as heads and feet of poultry and game birds and the bare tails of muskrats. Maybe this has physiological significance for the foxes. Maybe it is something that they do idly or in play.)

Undoubtedly civilized man, incidental to his use of the land, has done a great deal to make much of the world more livable for red foxes, if only through increasing their food supply. Apart from the increases of certain rodents and insects and what is collectively known as "farm game" that accompanied human exploitation of the virgin forests and prairies, man's poultry has been at least a locally im-

portant item of fox food. It is true that the more modern
poultry-raising establishments (together with many of the
less modern that have the services of efficient dogs) may
make their poultry unavailable to foxes, but an occasional
"hill-country" farm having chickens ranging all over the
place may provide the foxes with the nearest equivalent
of a "happy hunting ground" that foxes are likely to have.
Chickens that wander off among the rows of corn 100 to
200 yards away from farm buildings may give foxes some
of their best opportunities to seize a victim and be off with
it on what can be virtually a sustained-yield basis for
weeks.

Foxes do not invariably restrict their depredations on
poultry to outlying parts of fields. The most remarkable
poultry-raiding exploit of which I know was that of a
family group of foxes killing 160 chickens in two mornings
in a farmyard. In this instance, the young foxes were evidently being given "lessons in hunting" by their parents.
The efforts of a dogless and gunless housewife to protect
the flock were said to have made the raiding quite a sporting event for the young foxes, which romped and chased
over the yard like frolicsome puppies.

The dog theme can be carried on through accounts of
the hunting, caching, and scavenging of coyotes, wolves,
and other intelligent members of the dog family, domestic
dogs included. They can all show individualistic tactics,
ability to adjust to circumstances, and preferences for certain foods as well as reliance upon available staples.
Throughout whatever they do, their common doggishness
is always there.

RAPTORIAL BIRDS ARE the sight-hunting complements to
the nose-hunting predatory mammals. Although sense
of hearing may be of obvious help to such hunters as owls,
they still are watchers for opportunities to take the types
of prey that they are adapted to take. Granted that there
are great differences in what an owl hunting in dim light
and what a hawk soaring in bright daylight can see—particularly in view of the fact that some of the hawks must

have eyesight about as keen as that of anything on earth—
still the movements of prospective prey seem to be more
generally important than details of appearance in inviting
attack by predatory birds, whether hawks or owls.

The marsh hawk is the only raptorial bird whose
hunting habits I have thoroughly studied. As a graduate
student I studied the species in southern Wisconsin, in the
field, and in many experiments with captive hawks. Then
in northwest Iowa I participated in another program of
study similar to but an expansion of the one in Wisconsin.
In connection with the northwest Iowa studies, I had the
advantage of cooperating with W. J. Breckenridge[1] of the
University of Minnesota at the time that he was also carrying on an intensive study of marsh hawks near Anoka,
Minnesota.

The marsh hawk is a rangily built bird and is a comparatively slow pursuit flyer; but it can strike quickly with
its long legs and it can show remarkable agility within a
short striking radius. In flight, it can turn on its back to
strike upward. It can dip down quickly while flying low
over a field or marsh, and this permits effective surprise
tactics where the prey frequents small openings in tall
grass or in bushy or weedy vegetation or between rush and
reed clumps. That is the way it hunts; ready to dip and
grab; watching for something that moves; quartering over
grain fields, pastures, meadows, bogs, marshes, and up and
down stream valleys.

It is not a very strong hawk and its usual size range of
prey is from mice to half-grown cottontail rabbits, from
sparrows to flickers, quail, and half-grown domestic chickens. Exceptionally large sizes of prey may be the adults of
coots, bluewinged teal, Hungarian partridges, and Frank-
lin's ground squirrels. Birds of in between sizes taken as
prey include blackbirds, redheaded woodpeckers, meadowlarks, sora and Virginia rails; also mourning doves of all
ages but mostly immature, young pheasants, young partridges, and killdeers, and whatever other shorebirds happen to be catchable and manageable. Some of these may
be staple items locally while they remain highly available.
Frogs and garter snakes may be common dietary items, as
well as grasshoppers and other large insects.

Dick and Karen:

Thanks for putting up with us over the weekend. The hospitality and the food were great.

Thought you'd enjoy Paul Errington's new book. Note also the illustrations by Dyce M.

all the best — Jim

Adult marsh hawks are so much more accomplished as hunters than the young that they may seldom have to hunt during the middle of the day, except during the rearing season when they have dependent young to feed. When the demands of their young are heavy, the older hawks respond quickly to passing opportunities and exploit advantages while they have a chance. If they learn that the young ground squirrels of a particular hillside are not too clever about taking care of themselves, the old marsh hawks may return again and again as long as they can make catches. If a hunting adult discovers a not-quite-ready-to-fly brood of meadowlarks, it may grab here and there, killing or injuring most or all of the brood, then carry the prey home to the nest, one victim at a time. This is the sort of behavior that partly explains the "waves" of some prey species that may appear at a hawk nest.

I have observed these "waves" many times—several individuals in succession of a certain size of ground squirrel or yellow-headed blackbird or pheasant or flicker being brought in for a day or two. I do not contend that marsh hawks never show food preferences or that their prey may not to some extent consist of species sought primarily because the hawks like them for food. But when one finds a "wave" of such extraordinary prey as young screech owls, I am sure that it is not because the hawks found the owls especially delectable.

For young marsh hawks, the hunting pattern is similar to that for the old ones, except for the modifications forced by hunger and the trial and error of inexperience. Over and over, back and forth, one place and then another.

Young marsh hawks of late summer and fall are the most palpably hungry creatures. They may be seen hunting throughout the daylight hours, making one futile pass after another at intended prey that dodges, dives, whisks into vegetation, or counterattacks. I have thought that young marsh hawks must be, inherently, among the hungrier of creatures and among those naturally the more impatient of delays in feeding when they are hungry.

Many years ago, one of my experimentally hand-reared marsh hawks was so tame that, after banding it, I let it live unconfined and as independently as possible in heavy backyard vegetation resembling the type of place where young marsh hawks normally lived at a similar stage of their development. It was, nevertheless, too young to try hunting for itself, and I took food to it as often as parent hawks were feeding their young in the wild. Each time that I went forth to feed it, the frantic, screaming youngster came running and flapping or flying out of the shrubbery and tall grass to meet me, and I had to watch closely to avoid having a swift talon stroke snag a finger along with the ground squirrel or blackbird or piece of traffic-killed rabbit that I might be bringing. The hawk might be so excited that it would scream and tremble and bite too hastily to tear off enough meat to swallow, even from food material that it was accustomed to handling.

A few weeks further along in its development such a bird, if living wild, would be "on its own." As a killer of its own food, it would have very limited proficiency, and the prey that it could catch and subdue on its wetland and prairie hunting grounds would be grasshoppers, crickets, beetles, crayfishes traveling overland, small snakes—in short, about what a man could catch by hand without greatly exerting himself. With increasing proficiency in flying, swooping, and grabbing, the hawk would get some frogs, mice, and small birds.

The young hawk may have a hard time with something that is too weak or clumsy to escape or protect itself yet too big or tough to be killed by weak talons. Such a victim may be held and bitten rather haphazardly about breast or neck until vitals are torn. It may be eaten upon while still living and struggling. Considering what I have learned in detail about marsh hawk nervousness and hunger reactions from tame young hawks, I do not feel surprised when messy predation occurs on the part of newly hunting young hawks trying to feed themselves.

Perhaps the young marsh hawk might attack something like a cock pheasant or a barnyard rooster and get beaten off. Perhaps it might learn that it gained nothing from diving at flocks of coots or teal that only got up and flew a short distance before dropping down on the water again, or from passing at shorebirds that milled about in the air without letting themselves be caught. At any rate, we have the common late summer sight of grown pheasants and coots and ducks being watchful when marsh hawks sail over them but otherwise apparently conscious of their essential ineligibility as marsh hawk prey.

In addition to the food that young marsh hawks succeed in getting through their own predatory efforts, they scavenge on the leavings of older hawks or of other species of predators and, of course, on the conspicuous carrion of roadsides, beaches, and fields. The featherstrewn site of a dead chicken in a field is advertisement enough for a ravenous young marsh hawk. The time of maximum abundance and hence traffic mortality of roadside wildlife coincides with the time of maximum hunger for the self-hunting young marsh hawks, and the hawks may often feed on roadside carrion if not too frightened by the traffic. With the opening of the fall hunting season for waterfowl and upland game in the north-central region, dead and shot-crippled game constitute another source of food for marsh hawks and any other flesh-eating birds that can find and take advantage of it.

By winter, marsh hawks are largely gone from the region of my familiarity, but the few that sometimes remain may illustrate with clear simplicity what life can be for predators and prey. Let us say that the winter has been mild and that the southern Wisconsin or central Iowa fields are much as they were in late fall, with some flickers, meadowlarks, mourning doves, and marsh hawks still dallying around. The marsh hawks are living chiefly on the meadow mice that run along trails in grass or across openings between refuges and sources of food. Then a heavy snowfall covers everything and the marsh hawks find hunting unrewarding for a few days. Some of the more restless of the mice lay down back-and-forth trails on the surface of the snow in places and marsh hawks may dip and alight on these trails. They may lift talons out of the snow, empty, or grasping something that squirms around trying to bite. The juncos and tree sparrows do pretty much the right thing—they are not helpless—when marsh hawks sail over the weedy growths where small seed-eating birds feed.

MARSH HAWK

The bluejays frequenting the edges of wood lots have the right answers also, as do the chickadees and associated tree birds that do not need to go out where marsh hawks have much chance of catching them. The midwinter fox squirrels, rabbits, and pheasants generally do not have to let themselves be caught and killed by marsh hawks either.

A week of this and the marsh hawks may be hungry, but the seed-eaters that no longer have access to their seeds may not only be hungry but weakening. A marsh hawk finds a mourning dove that it can catch and a couple more the next day. One of the best bets as a predatory objective, as well as one of the most conspicuous of all on the thick snow covering, may be a covey of quail that walks and pecks amid the corn stubble or dry weed plants out there in the open, 150 yards from brushy cover. Perhaps a marsh hawk makes a pass at the quail—and the quail get up and fly to the brush, three or four birds seeming to flutter a little in flight. Days later, a quail flushed by a marsh hawk alights on the snow before reaching the cover and the hawk keeps coming back to that place, or to some other place where quail are starving.

And about this time, unless melting of the snow soon exposes the ground, the marsh hawks may disappear from the neighborhood. Presumably they move far enough south, down into Missouri or southern Illinois, so as to winter again in the more snowless types of hunting grounds where living is less stringent for both marsh hawks and marsh hawk prey.

MY KNOWLEDGE OF the hunting methods of the great horned owl is unbalanced—about some aspects I know a good deal; about others I know little. I know that at night the owls sit in lookout trees or on telephone poles, rooftops, and haystacks, even on fence posts and muskrat lodges. They sweep on their noiseless wings over fields and meadows, over marshes and the edges of open water. They have a reputation for fierceness but, to me, they have always seemed more like matter-of-fact birds that did their hunting efficiently.

Of the tame raptorial birds with which I experimented as a graduate student, two of the hand-reared horned owls were the most non-predacious of flesh-eaters. They were in adult plumage and equipped with some of the most formidable talons in North America. I remember them as I tried to give them experience in catching their own food before turning them loose, banded, to take care of themselves in the wild. My attempted training of these owls consisted of releasing live sparrows, mice, and rats into their cages, but the owls continued to be so lacking in predatory inclinations that I was sure they would starve if forced to do their own hunting. I could not take them with me when I left Wisconsin, so had to find another home for them. Later I was informed that one of these pets had killed and eaten the other, but it took a long time for either of them to learn that talons were weapons.

Another of my young horned owls was brought in from its parental nest when about a quarter grown. It never did become a pet, though it would tolerate discreet handling. When I put live sparrows, mice, and rats into its cage it grappled and ate them as if it knew what to do, and it quickly gained expertness with practice. However, it would not attack the Belgian hare and the guinea pig that I tried out on it; and it was so panicked by the blindly rushing guinea pig that it flew up and clung to the roof of the cage. The incident of the guinea pig was such a shock to the morale of this owl that it would not kill even rats until a five-day fast forced it to behave like a predator again. After its release, banded, in the University Arboretum, it took care of itself for nearly six months before a hunter shot it four miles away.

From my years of field studies and the examination of thousands of horned owl pellets, I have concluded that the horned owl seems to take, within a certain size range, what happens to be most convenient for it to catch and handle. Domestic geese and turkeys, minks, striped skunks, and opossums are about as large or as formidable prey as North American horned owls kill. Smaller prey items include May beetles, carrion beetles, wolf spiders, and cutworms. I have seen large horned owl pellets that were solid masses of cutworm heads and skins. This diet of small items, including grasshoppers, crickets and snakes, represents much of what the clumsy young owls are apt to find for themselves in late summer after their parents refuse to feed them any longer.

The great importance of cottontail rabbits in the diets of horned owls living in north-central agricultural communities leads to the question of whether the owls may prey selectively upon the rabbits. I recognize that there could be some selection, that the owls may be aware that the cottontails offer them—in size, manageability, and edibility—a particular advantage as prey. Yet, it has long seemed to me that cottontails are so much preyed upon by the owls because they are usually conspicuous, abundant, and available in the places where the owls usually hunt.

Weakness, as such, does not seem especially to predispose quail to horned owl predation, but restlessness does. Movements of starving quail into strange or uninhabitable places are an invitation to predation anywhere. There may be some bickering at dusk in a quail covey that has too many birds or has a strange bird or two in it. There may be a night flush by a mammal, and scattered birds trying to do something with themselves out on the moonlit snow and not finding any place that gives them good protection. In the early dawn, there may be some preoccupation of covey members with the objectionable traits of their fellows, as late winter grades into spring and brings out more and more short-tempered friction with the beginning of pairing. A quail that is where it does not belong, or is doing something unsafe, or has its attention diverted, can be more eligible for a horned owl's next meal than the next catchable rabbit. Then quail feathers may float down from a branch, and forequarters of quail appear in one horned owl pellet and hindquarters in another.

Mice may be, in the aggregate, an important horned owl food. When meadow mice overrun the fields during one of their abundance peaks, horned owls may feed upon them more than upon their usual rabbits; at other times, mice may show up hardly at all in horned owl pellets. Sometimes remains of lemming mice may predominate, but in the north-central region this species of mouse lives in special niches which are only occasionally found in the hunting grounds of local owls. Of all of the mice in our region, the deer mice seem to be taken with the nearest approach to regularity, and I think that I understand why. They are more likely to be present in fair abundance the year around and from year to year, and they may engage in considerable running across snow, climbing in bushes, or even wandering far out in open spaces.

Short-tailed shrews—mouselike in appearance but very different from mice—may be heavily preyed upon by horned (and other) owls when numerous and active in places where owls catch them. The voracity of shrews resulting from their high metabolic rates keeps them busy searching for food, often running on top of the snow as well as burrowing through it. They can be more abundant and available than mice, and owls gulp them down despite the unpleasant flavor they, along with moles, patently have for such discriminating predators as foxes.

Moles are vulnerable to seizure by powerful birds of

prey as they burrow the surface soil or push out earth or as they may wander over the surface of ground or snow.

Pocket gophers are vulnerable to horned owls as they, even more than moles, push out heaps of earth during their burrowing. R. D. Bird[2] found pocket gopher remains in 16 of 114 horned owl pellets from southern Manitoba and commented on the special vulnerability of the gophers in May, when they spend much time above ground during their mating season.

Another rodent that may be little seen by human eyes, yet frequently eaten by horned owls, is the flying squirrel. I have wondered if its nocturnal activities and gliding habits might make it vulnerable to the owls out of proportion to its numbers; but it also can be abundant locally and doubtless can have a substantial annual surplus to be frittered away somehow.

Weasels seem to be preyed upon by horned owls with exceptional severity in proportion to numbers. The weasels are nowhere abundant on my study areas—indeed, most of my study areas do not have any weasels on them during an ordinary winter, and the other areas show "sign" of perhaps one or two or three weasels per square mile. Weasel remains in 2 or 3 per cent of horned owl pellets therefore represent an intensity of predation that is hard to explain except in terms of the weasel's frequently incautious way of life.

I confess that, when it comes to understanding horned owl predation upon birds, I do not always know what to think. A marsh may have several thousand ducks and coots on it at a time when the horned owls living or nesting on its islands or wooded peninsulas may be eating cottontails and land birds—or eating blackbirds or grebes. Practically any of the small- to medium-sized birds may show up in the owl pellets, perhaps or perhaps not during heavy runs of some other prey items. The screech owl is the bird that I would consider subject to the heaviest horned owl predation in relation to its abundance on my north-central study areas. There must be, in fact, a special hazard for screech owls hunting in horned owl range, though the screech owls plainly can maintain passable abundance despite the horned owls, even when living in the same tracts of woods.

Ordinarily, horned owl predation upon poultry is centered upon birds that roost outside of buildings, as in trees about some farmyard that the owls have learned to visit. However at a ranch where I once lived in western South Dakota, horned owls were known to enter a cattle shed to take roosting chickens. For reasons of their hunting habits, these owls that visit the vicinities of farmyards also are in a position to catch domestic pigeons and English sparrows—or the house mice and barn rats. As the owls sit on their lookout perches awaiting opportunities to catch something, they do not seem to care especially if their prey is a bird or a mammal.

Horned owl predation upon snakes and fishes may either occur as the owls happen to encounter an occasional snake or some half-stranded fish during their usual hunting forays, or as snakes or fishes may be vulnerably concentrated in special places. A lake shore may have frogs and frog-eating snakes, and droughts may concentrate snakes as well as snake prey about the remaining water holes of a stream. Horned owls obviously have no compunction about taking advantage of both when that represents easy hunting. The snakes ordinarily taken are garter snakes or hognosed snakes, together with smaller individuals of bull snakes and fox snakes. Fishes taken may be up to or over a pound in weight, mostly scaly fishes such as suckers, carp, and sunfishes; I think that they are "specialized" upon by the owls chiefly because they are discovered in shallows with their backs partly protruding out of the water.

Among the other cold-blooded vertebrates serving as horned owl prey, tiger salamanders may be only sporadically available during most of the warm weather months and the owls pick up one now and then. But briefly, at certain times and places, the salamanders may be just about everywhere, and an observer should not need to strain to understand how horned owls get all of them that they want to eat. I remember a three-day period of warm, wet spring weather in southern Wisconsin, with salamanders crawling over the ground and horned owls apparently eating little else. I can also remember early fall migrations of salamanders across a wide strip of nearly bare sand along the shore of a South Dakota marsh, and it was easy to see then, too, how predators wanting to eat salamanders could have done so.

From Gulf Coast to northern tundras and from ocean to ocean across the continent, our North American horned owls, in their different geographical races, live practically everywhere that conditions are suitable for them. They live in woodlands of the Southeast, amid the canyons of the Southwest, in desert and high plains and mountainous regions. They live in prairie and woodland farming communities, in the Ozarks, and in the real North Woods. Wherever the species lives, one patent reason for its living is its capacity for exploiting what it needs of the local food resources.

It does lack the advantage of being an efficient scavenger, although as a species it is not too proud to eat meat that it does not kill—if it finds it. I once studied a pair of horned owls that fed on a man-skinned cow carcass lying in a wood lot, and lesser examples of scavenging may occasionally be found along roadsides and lake shores. Rarely, during my fur-trapping years, a horned owl took a rabbit from one of my snares or was attracted to bloody rabbit remains used as trap bait. The horned owl simply is not one of the most adept of creatures at finding suitable material on which to scavenge.

But at detecting, seizing, and killing a wide variety of living things that move, the horned owl still shows enough proficiency to feed itself well wherever any owls would stand much chance of feeding. As predators go, it, like the mink, is a good "general practitioner."

THE BARRED OWL'S environmental niches overlap those of the horned owl in the north-central region, but the barred owl may be considered somewhat (not entirely) more a bird of deep woods and wooded river bottomlands. It is much weaker than the horned owl and lacks the horned owl's capabilities for swift flight. I think of it as being more of a shy and spooky bird—though its raucous caterwauling at night does not sound shy.

In its food habits, the barred owl seldom takes anything larger than a one-third grown cottontail rabbit, a flicker, or a screech owl. Quail may be taken when highly vulnerable, though usually some other predator gets the vulnerable quail before the barred owl does. Pheasants and poultry soon outgrow the size range of barred owl prey; besides, they are rather unlikely to frequent places hunted over by barred owls. Small birds of woodland species, deer mice, shrews, moles, flying squirrels, crayfishes, woodland snakes and frogs and salamanders, fishes of woodland pools, and the larger sizes of woodland insects are the forms upon which we find the barred owl preying.

OF COURSE IT IS to be expected that the nocturnal flying squirrels should be preyed upon by night-hunting owls if anything preys upon them; that daylight-active squirrels should be taken by day-hunting hawks; that night-hunting

BARRED OWL

small owls should be taken by night-hunting large owls. But that does not mean that small owls cannot be preyed upon by day-hunting predators, nor that diurnal squirrels cannot be preyed upon by night hunters, nor any denial of things that happen in Nature.

The role of availability of prey in governing food habits of predators may well be illustrated by the predation borne by the inhabitants of some particular type of environment that is hunted over by various predators. Bottomland woods may be frequented by both horned owls and barred owls, and there the diets of both species of owls run to the woodland birds and mice, the moles and shrews, the small cold-blooded vertebrates, the crayfishes, the May beetles, stag beetles, ground beetles, and carrion beetles. Then we find the diets of broadwinged and red-shouldered hawks in such places much the same as the diets of the owls, except that these hawks are not as adept at catching birds and are more likely than the owls to catch snakes. If we add the Cooper's hawk to the deep woods equation and compare the food habits of hawks collectively with those of owls collectively, we can see that many prey groups suffer fairly similar predatory pressures day and night.

The basic availability of prey to predators may be further exemplified by the insignificant differences in the food habits of red and gray foxes living in a particular area. The food habits of feral house cats—the big, free ranging, wild tomcats of woods and fields—may resemble the food habits of the foxes, despite differences in body build and hunting tactics of cats and foxes.

But all of this does not mean that we should ignore what evidence we have of specialized predation or specialized protection. In the matter of specialized hunting habits, a predator such as a red fox (which may have many alternatives to choose from yet may elect to take some particular type of prey) is capable of developing exceptional degrees of predacious facility. A peregrine falcon specializing on domestic pigeons is probably able to catch them if any wild predator can and with a minimal expenditure of exacting effort. Lesser degrees of profi-

ciency on the part of such other mammalian or bird predators that specialize to some extent must also be advantageous to the hunters at times.

It should be pointed out that when predatory skill
becomes so great as to arouse terror in favorite prey species, it may partly nullify itself. All-day "freezing" on the
part of scattered members of a quail covey attended by a
Cooper's hawk goes far toward making them unavailable
to the hawk. I have often observed in my own extensive
hunting experience how little shooting may be required
to thoroughly "wise-up" an adaptable game population,
and counterparts to this surely are to be found in numerous predator-prey relationships in the wild. The extent
to which wild populations are "wised-up" most of the time
with respect to their racial enemies is in one way illustrated by the large proportion of predatory attempts that
may be observed to fail under ordinary field conditions.

Gustav Rudebeck,[3] who made exceptionally good observations on predatory behavior of hawks and eagles in
southern Sweden, found that only a small proportion of
the serious predatory attempts that he witnessed were successful. For the bird-hunting European sparrow hawk, he
recorded a total of 22 victims taken in probably about 500
completed attacks and attempts at seizure. At least the
sight-hunting predators, though willing and ready to attack, do not even attempt attacks in a large proportion of
the cases in which they see prospective prey within ordinary attacking distances. It is apparent that they do
some appraising of their chances for success on the basis
of preliminary responsiveness of the prey before launching
forth in an actual attack. Or, they may feint and then
follow through if the prey betrays some uncertainty or
physical weakness.

When it comes to human appraisals of what predation
is like from the standpoint of the predators, I think that
we are on safe grounds if we assume that any simple predatory feat that man can accomplish without artificial
weapons, such as catching and killing with bare hands,
would also be within the power of a great many other predators. Man along with many other predators could catch

starving quail in the snow, or crayfishes, garter snakes, frogs, stranded fishes, fledgling birds, grasshoppers, and mice where these are everywhere abundant; he could rob a nest of bird or turtle or snake eggs if he felt like it; he could find a certain amount of edible carrion by searching for it or by happening upon it.

Nevertheless, in projecting himself into a wild predator's place, man can make some fallacious assumptions, even if he can imagine what it would mean to possess a goshawk's faculty for swift pursuit through the brush, an owl's silent flight, or the extreme keenness of hearing, sight, or smell that certain predators have. One assumption I long made was that the breeding season calls of birds would make them markedly vulnerable to predation through advertising their presence to predatory opportunists, but I learned, in time, that drumming ruffed grouse or "bob-whiting" quail did not necessarily lack awareness of what went on about them.

A drumming ruffed grouse on a log about thirty feet from a cabin window gave me my best lessons on how such a bird could be alert even when engaged in an act that seemed thoroughly to occupy its attention. After sneaking up to behind the window I would stand back in the shadow to watch, then experimentally make some little sound—such as creaking a board in the floor—to see if the grouse would notice it at the height of the drumming. It would "freeze" at any stage of its ritual (including drumming periods) in the half-light of early morning or at dusk. It might slip off the log to disappear in the ground cover. It might glide easily into the aspens down the hill.

I am sure that a wide variety of prospective prey species show similar alertness much of the time when they do not have to let themselves be caught. Adaptable prey species that have learned about their enemies through racial testing over the millennia seem to have the answer for most predatory attacks as long as they are not trying to live under a disadvantage; and the predators can do little about them except to tend to their own business of living in their turn, to seek what opportunities for exploitation they can. The predators may have their staples in teeming populations of mice, rabbits, grasshoppers, or crayfishes. Or, sooner or later, something overproduces, something is evicted, something is up against an emergency from fire or flood or snow, something is too young or too old or too sick to take care of itself, something does the wrong thing or becomes available to predators by accident; and the predators respond, exactly as they also have become conditioned to do over the millennia that particular species of predators and prey have lived with each other.

4

FANGS AND TALONS
AND DOG EAT DOG

THERE SEEMS TO EXIST something of a traditional concept that predation by predators upon predators falls in a category separate and different from other categories of predation. Birds and beasts of talon and fang are supposed to maintain a chivalrous attitude toward each other—ready to fight in defense of their rights, yes, but otherwise conducting themselves according to the sort of code to which the higher grades of plundering humans are said to adhere. By the expression "dog eat dog" man at least implies scorn for the breaking of a code.

However that may be, there is much evidence that predator does prey upon predator and that such predation is not always restricted to times and places of unusual food scarcity.

THAT FORMIDABLE GENERAL feeder, the great horned owl, is the one predator in particular known to have preyed upon other predators on my study areas. In addition to the screech owls and weasels and skunks that seem to be so vulnerable to the horned owls, just about the whole array of predatory mammals and birds of small to medium sizes may be represented in horned owl diets. Our north-central records of horned owl victims include minks, a

GREAT HORNED OWL AND MINK

young fox, sparrow hawks, sharpshinned and Cooper's hawks, a possible goshawk and a nestling redtail, many longeared and shorteared owls, barred owl, burrowing owl, Richardson's owl, and saw-whet owl. There is also no doubt that the horned owl occasionally attacks a house cat, and an interesting situation has been described in Missouri where a winter roost of marsh hawks drew horned owl predation.

The German ornithologist, Otto Uttendörfer,[4] studied the food habits of the horned owl's larger relative, the eagle owl, in Europe. About 6 per cent of the eagle owl's diet consisted of predatory mammals and birds—weasels, hawks, and owls in about equal proportions but including among about 5,500 items five each of house cats and young foxes, an osprey, nine goshawks, and fifteen peregrine falcons. Yngvar Hagen,[5] in a fine study of Norwegian birds of prey, found that nearly 10 per cent of the bird prey items taken by eagle owls were hawks and owls—the most formidable being a snowy owl.

In Uttendörfer's summary of over 8,300 bird items taken by goshawks, over 6 per cent were small to medium sizes of hawks and owls, and the mammalian items included a house cat and a young fox. Both Uttendörfer and Hagen listed weasels as prey of almost all European hawks and owls, and small hawks and owls as prey of the larger ones.

Except for the horned owl, the data on food habits of birds of prey in north-central United States show only sporadic preying upon what we might call "real" predators. I have known a barred owl to take a small mink, and redtailed hawks to take minks and a young horned owl. Five of 50 vertebrate items found by P. F. English[6] in a Michigan redtail nest were weasels. A rather special item of prairie falcon prey in the West was a bobcat kitten.

Food habits of eagles may be exceptionally hard to interpret, insofar as the eagles are not only formidable predators but some of them also have propensities for carrion-eating and robbing other predators. However, the golden eagle is usually quite predacious, and its food items may represent more killed prey than may the food items of the bald eagle and its close relatives.

S. K. Carnie[7] recorded for the nests of golden eagles in California over five hundred vertebrate items, of which over 5 per cent were carnivores, mostly skunks but including four house cats, two raccoons, and a gray fox. Large birds of prey (mostly great horned owls) comprised another 2 per cent. Other North American literature mentions a goshawk, martens, and young wolves as prey of golden eagles. Among seventy-seven mammalian items listed by Uttendörfer for European golden eagles were a house cat, five arctic foxes, four red foxes, and two foxes eaten upon as carrion; among fifty-nine bird items, a gyrfalcon. Citing numerous Old World authors, Uttendörfer prepared a list of prey items for the golden eagle that included pole-cat, young lynx, and badger, besides the expected weasels, foxes, and miscellaneous hawks and owls. One Rouman-ian nest contained a red fox and heads of eight house cats. Among 129 items found in Estonian nests were two mar-tens, two polecats, three red foxes, a young dog, two buz-zards, and a tawny owl.

T. G. SCOTT AND I EXAMINED over four thousand food items cached or left about feeding places or dens by Iowa red foxes, nearly six thousand fox droppings, and over five hundred stomach and intestinal tracts. The food items differed with the locality but were much as one might expect anywhere for an animal possessed of red fox psy-chology and physical attributes. The predatory forms taken were chiefly members of the weasel family, from weasels and skunks to badgers. Other items: a raccoon, a young horned owl, and an enormous snapping turtle.

The most remarkable predatory exploit on the part of a red fox of which I know was that of a Finnish fox that killed and ate an otter after a savage and prolonged battle in which the fox was the aggressor throughout. Red foxes also may prey upon arctic foxes that they find at a disad-vantage.

EAGLE OWL

Of the northern hemisphere foxes, the arctic fox may very literally give us the best examples of "dog eat dog" as part of a way of life. Adapted to live in what can be for many months of the year a grimly food-poor environment, the species may scavenge upon dead of its own kind (including foxes caught in traps). Furthermore, the literature contains references to fighting and cannibalism at times of food scarcity—of animals eating each other out on the sea ice and of hungry mothers eating their young.

The coyote, bigger and more powerful than any of the foxes associated with it in North America, has capabilities of taking more formidable prey, including prey species that are themselves predatory. C. C. Sperry[8] summarized the contents of over 8,300 food-containing coyote stomachs examined by U.S. government personnel. Of these, nearly 2 per cent contained carnivore remains other than coyote remains, mostly skunk, badger, weasel, and bobcat, in that order. There were also seven representations of three species of foxes and three of the rare black-footed ferret—also thirty-five of birds of prey, including two of great horned owls. Of nearly fourteen thousand items of coyote food listed by other authors in western United States, nineteen were of skunks, three of minks, two of badger, two of gray fox, fourteen of bobcat, two of house cat, one of ring-tailed cat, and five of raccoon.

Coyotes are well known for the feeding they do on the bodies of other coyotes in "coyote country." Coyote remains occurred in 224 of the stomachs in the Sperry series, and Adolph Murie[9] found evidence of coyotes doing this sort of feeding even when other food was available. It may be doubted that very much of the coyote cannibalism is predatory.

Wolves may prey upon all smaller members of the dog family, and upon lynxes and wolverines. A lone wolf is said not to be able to handle a wolverine, but several wolves can. However, wolves may avoid attacking a wolverine because of the unpleasant odor it releases when attacked. Most fights between wolves and bears of which I have read seemed to have ended inconclusively.

We need not restrict our attention to wild animals in considering predator versus predator. A tame house cat can kill a weasel just as dead as a horned owl can, and there may be little difference between the killing power of a pack of formidable yet thoroughly domesticated hunting dogs and so many wild wolves. During a trip into the northern Ontario "bush" in my youth, I became acquainted with a sledge dog that had gotten free of its chain on three successive nights, and on each night it had killed another sledge dog. I once deciphered from tracks in snow and the body of a small house cat the story of how a gray fox had intercepted the cat along a trail, seized it, tossed it in the air, and killed it by a bite through the brain; and this was not without its dramatic aspects. Nev-

ertheless, to me, it is the predation by and between wild
animals that is the most interesting.

The old enmities between cats and dogs take on a
particular vividness if we go on past the house animals, to
consider the relations between cats and dogs that are still
undoubtedly wild. We may be confident that the major
groups of cat animals—up to lions, tigers, and the extinct
saber-tooth—have had troublous experiences with pack-
hunting wild dogs or even with lone individuals under
some circumstances. But the big cats can also prey upon
some of the wild dogs when they have opportunities. The
lynx in northern North America and northern Eurasia
can be one of the most successful of predators upon red
foxes, especially when the foxes are handicapped by deep
loose snow that continues to hold up the hairy winter
"snowshoes" of the lynx. Instances are reported of individual lynxes killing two or three foxes in a night,
though unless very hungry a lynx may not eat of its fox
victims. In addition to preying upon foxes, northern hemisphere lynxes have been known to prey upon minks, martens, badgers, wildcats, dogs, and young wolves.

The wide variety of prey taken by a close relative of
the lynx, the North American bobcat, is illustrated not
only by field observations of many people but also by considerable specimen data on food habits. Bobcats rather
frequently prey upon skunks and foxes and one stomach
contained remains of a young Canada lynx.

The prey list of that larger American cat, the cougar,
includes skunks, martens, badgers, coyotes, foxes, young
cougars, raccoons, and black bears.

If we go on to consider predacious activities of the
larger predatory mammals other than cats and dogs, we
can find references to the wolverine preying upon arctic
fox, lynx, and otter, to the otter preying upon the mink,
to the fisher preying upon the marten, to bears preying
upon other bears.

IN MANY CASES the distinctions between predatory intentions and antagonistic attacks by one predator upon

another are difficult to make. We may read of fights of jaguar against cougar, coyote against badger or bobcat, goshawk against horned owl, peregrine falcon against some other formidable hawk or owl, and some of these fights may be deadly. Many fights between different species of predators are not unlike the hostile encounters of rivals of the same species, in defense of young or of territories; or they may be manifestations of some other kind of intolerance. Mobbing (or its individual equivalent) may be a common response of the falcon or "blue-darter" type of hawk to the presence of other birds of prey, especially horned owls. And certainly most mammals and birds adapted for a predatory existence are capable of just plain anger or desperation when having trouble with some other predator. Strife between possessors of weapons can result in consequences ranging from a few harmless passes to a thorough mauling or killing. If a dead victim lies there on the ground it may be treated as prey (or as some other "property," perhaps as a scent station) or it may be henceforth ignored by the killer.

Some strife clearly results from one predator robbing or attempting to rob another predator of its prey. Adolph Murie[10] saw wolves viciously harassing grizzly bears that habitually appropriated the caches and fresh prey of the wolves. Although bears seem to show a special disposition for bullying lesser predators away from their prey, much of this sort of behavior is shown by other predators. In the Far North, almost any flesh-eater may bully whatever is to be bullied whenever food can thus be obtained. In more hospitable regions, we may see the well-known bullying attacks of eagles upon ospreys having fishes, and so on. The bullied creatures may not be able to do anything about it in most cases, but sometimes they try to, and sometimes they put up a successful or even a deadly defense.

Then, there are the "sporting" attacks, usually directed against non-predacious animals but sometimes against predators, too. They may be the rushes and nips of coyotes bedeviling a wolf or a bear, the swoops of an eagle at a coyote, of a peregrine falcon at a redshouldered hawk, of an agile small "blue-darter" at almost any large clumsy hawk. But mock fights can turn into real fights, and rough predatory games can grade off into dangerous ones when weaponed participants become excited.

I never found cannibalism, in the sense of a predator eating a member of the same species, occurring frequently in my own studies of predatory mammals and birds. Most examples that I have are of young animals eaten by either their stronger litter or nest mates or by their parents. When such victims were weak or ailing individuals, it often was impossible to ascertain whether they were killed or merely eaten as carrion. The last owlet to hatch in a clutch of eggs would be a most likely prospective victim if its nest mates were too successful in competing with it for food brought to the nest. Or, a mother fox or raccoon might eat one of her newborn young along with its placenta. It seems to be a common experience of zoo keepers to find carnivorous mothers eating their ailing young or eating their young in response to psychological upsets.

If sufficiently hungry, practically any wild flesh-eater at any stage of development may eat on the body of another. In some types of cannibalism it may even appear that the best food for the species is none other than its own kind, especially at certain stages in the development of the young. Kenneth D. Carlander of Iowa State University told me of having seen a string of eight northern pike fingerlings, each individual about two inches long, with the last seven individuals in the string each grasping in its mouth and digesting away the tail of the one ahead of it. Still, when it comes to actual predation by adult upon adult of the same species, we can expect mutual respect toward each other's prowess to inhibit a certain

WOLVES HARASSING GRIZZLY BEARS . . .

amount of predatory behavior. Goshawks preying upon goshawks, or horned owls upon horned owls, would find such predation a hard way to make a regular living even if plenty of goshawks or horned owls existed to be preyed upon.

I do not wish to generalize overmuch in the above connection, however. Great variation has been observed in individual temperaments within species of hawks, owls, and members of the dog family. Moreover, it is plain that the hazards of attacking equals or near equals do not always deter attacks.

WHAT IS THE POPULATION effect of all of this fang against fang and talon against talon, of shedders of blood having their own blood shed?

I am not alone in thinking that weasels may suffer enough predation to keep their numbers at lower levels than otherwise would be maintained. Roger M. Latham,[11] after commenting upon the frequency with which foxes killed weasels without eating them, showed that, in general, Pennsylvania weasel populations declined as foxes reached their higher population levels, both on a county wide scale and over the state as a whole. Yngvar Hagen regarded predation by predators upon other predators as being a biological factor of great significance in Norway, especially at times of pronounced shortage of staple prey. After "cyclic" collapses of mouse or lemming or hare populations, the hungry predators of some northern regions may have little available to eat except each other.

I think that situations inviting really severe predation

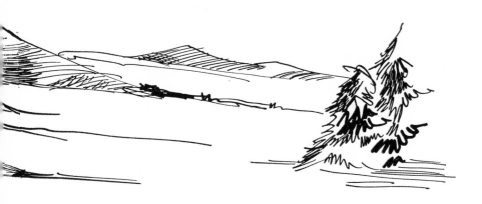

by warm-blooded predators upon other predators are rather exceptional. On the whole, I should say that the predators themselves seem to be killed or preyed upon about as other wild animals are, in proportion to their availability or vulnerability, or according to whatever makes sense in natural relationships.

We can often see the same old "biological eight ball" operating when this or that predator itself falls victim to predation. Predators, too, pass through vulnerable stages when young. Overproduced or evicted predators get into unfamiliar or inhospitable places or wander around where they do not belong. They may suffer disadvantages because of hunger or weather emergencies such as ice storms or deep snows or intense cold. An ailing predator may mope or blunder around like anything else that is ailing, and predators have their injuries and grow old.

Man may call predators robber barons or cannibals and talk of honor or lack of honor among thieves as applying to natural wild animals. For myself, I have no objection to people romanticizing or anthropomorphizing Nature as long as they do it in a pleasant and whimsical manner that no one would take seriously. But when it comes to seeing nobility or depravity in the natural behavior of wild animals because they possess or lack qualities that man would regard as honorable, I think that we should always remember that the moral rightness or wrongness that man sees in these relationships is, after all, only man's.

In "dog eat dog" relationships among wild animals, a young horned owl does nothing reprehensible when it eats its young nest mate. Neither does a wolf pack that rips a coyote to pieces and scatters the pieces in a frolic. Nor does a fox that snaps up a weasel to leave it lying dead beside a trail do a worthy deed in ridding the world of the kind of animal that man might call a cruel and bloodthirsty little monster. It would be best if we just regarded wild animals as living things being themselves, the killers and non-killers, alike.

PART TWO:

OF CASES AND CONDITIONS

5

PREDATION AND
THE BOBWHITE QUAIL:
SOME COMFORTABLE
GENERALIZATIONS

MY OVERALL RESPONSIBILITY under my graduate fellowship at the University of Wisconsin, midyear 1929 to midyear 1932, was to study the ecology of the bobwhite quail. H. L. Stoddard[12] had completed his classic quail investigation in Georgia and Florida, and to some extent my fellowship assignment in Wisconsin was to see whether his findings would apply at the opposite extreme of the bobwhite's geographic range.

The ecology of any living species is a sufficiently big subject to allow a variety of approaches. I made the study of quail mortality my specialty because I felt that this approach was the way to an understanding of limiting factors and because my years of hunting and fur trapping had given me a proficiency in "reading sign." In studying mortality I made a further specialty of predation upon the quail, not only to obtain information on the principal types of predation suffered by the quail but also better to appraise effects of the predation upon the quail populations.

I located hawk and owl nests, gathered hawk and owl pellets and prey remains, and experimented with captive birds of prey to learn about feeding techniques and the kinds of bill marks left on feathers. I examined stomachs of foxes killed by hunters, stomachs of anything predatory

I found dead (as on highways), droppings, and remains of prey left about the entrances of dens. I watched such places as were likely to be frequented by both quail and their predatory enemies.

Some of this was not enjoyable. I might be trying to sit still and watch with field glasses while the mosquitoes bit; in those days we had no effective insect repellents. Specimen material could be smelly or messy. I have had to search in the mud of a farmer's hog lot to find fox carcasses needed for stomach examinations. After walking all day up and down hills or wading snow, I might have to work until midnight or later to take care of what I had brought into the laboratory. Or, the material that I did get might be very nearly unmanageable—spoiled or digested away or fragmentary beyond recognition.

On the other hand, it might be a sunny fall day, and I might be lying on a rocky ledge watching redtailed hawks as they circled and circled or perched in lookout trees, and haze would soften the changing colors of wooded valleys and hills. At almost any time I might see special sights— flying squirrels out in daylight, otter tracks along a bottomland creek, peregrine falcons overhead screaming at me from above a nesting ledge, or something else worth seeing that might not have any great bearing on quail mortality. (I remember eleven ruffed grouse bursting out of a juniper thicket one at a time, all flying evenly spaced at the same speed and in the same direction, and I aimed my finger and said "pow," as each one reached ideal shotgun range.)

In results accomplished, I could not always be sure that I learned anything of value from an entire day—or days—of hard work. Sometimes my day's notes would cover pages of paper, and I would have an excited yet comfortable feeling that I was getting somewhere.

MEADOW MICE (also called meadow voles) were excessively abundant during that first summer, fall, and winter of study in southern Wisconsin. Fields were riddled by their burrows, and the stocky little forms could be seen running through a network of paths. What I found was that, as long as these mice remained available prey for predators, almost everything predatory that could take advantage of them did so. The more versatile types of predators still took a considerable variety of other prey, but I saw little evidence of quail victims. A moss-grown, weathered owl pellet, believed datable to the previous winter of 1928–29, consisted of quail bones and gizzard contents of black locust and sweet clover seeds. This pellet went into a special repository in my office, where I could readily find it and spread it out on a sheet of paper to examine from time to time.

As soon as tracking snows came during my first winter in Wisconsin, I was able to obtain accurate counts of the quail populations then present on seven regularly observed study areas. These areas varied in size from 160 to 4,500 acres and totaled about 7,400 acres. In addition, I occasionally visited other areas not kept under regular observation in order to improve my perspective concerning the problems that wintering quail were up against on the northern fringe of their range. All of these areas were chosen because, together, they were representative of the quail environment to be found in southern Wisconsin. They varied in quality from some of the poorest to some of the best for quail in that part of the north-central region.

The area on which the wintering fortunes of quail populations could be followed with greatest satisfaction was the biggest, the one of 4,500 acres situated east of Prairie du Sac. No matter how desperate the quail coveys became on the Prairie du Sac area, most of them still remained within the 4,500 acres. This was partly because of the large size of the area, partly because of some natural barriers—not invariably effective—to winter movements of quail in and out of the area. One of the reasons why the Prairie du Sac area was set up as my principal study area was because it came as close to being a self-contained land unit, comparable to an ecological island, as any sizable quail-occupied tract that I found within convenient driving distance of my university headquarters.

The Prairie du Sac area was for other reasons an inviting place on which to work. It was in a former home neighborhood of Stoddard, who took me out there and introduced me to his old friends. One of them, Albert Gastrow, became my own close friend and companion. We walked together, whole days at a time, whenever the study program required up-to-date information as to how well the quail were getting along.

If conditions were favorable for counting tracks, we would start in one corner of the area, pick up the trail of a quail covey, count the tracks, follow the trail to where the covey was roosting, deliberately flush the birds so as to count them in the air and watch for weakening birds among them. Then on to the next covey or group of coveys, and so on, until we had as accurate a census as possible for a given part of the area. We learned how to decipher confusing trails, how to avoid misidentifying coveys in our censusing, and how best to locate particular coveys when we wanted to. We studied the propensities that individual coveys or groups of coveys might have for combining or splitting apart. We tried to learn what went wrong for them when something did go wrong.

All together, from late October to April, I devoted two-thirds of my daylight time to field studies on the seven observational areas.

Throughout this almost continual checking of quail populations, my main rule of procedure was to learn as much as possible while interfering the least with the normal way of life of the birds. Mere disturbance from flushing them in the daytime—the sort of thing that could happen whenever a farmer walked along a brushy fence row—was nothing to worry about, but I always avoided flushing in a snowstorm or interfering with the birds going to roost properly at night. My policy of non-interference with the fortunes of the quail also extended to periods of crisis, at least to a degree consistent with the purposes of the study program. When they were dying I usually let them die, just as quail always have died, without either relieving or aggravating their troubles.

Under favorable working conditions, the daily counts of birds in the coveys visited would usually be exact, and when they were not I would make an effort to obtain exact counts for doubtful coveys within a few days. Despite the spread of days between the beginning and the finishing of a census round on a large area like Prairie du Sac, the data fitted closely enough together to give census figures for the whole area, for early and late winter and for some times in between. I would later learn from experience that the accuracy of direct counts fell as the numbers of wintering quail approached or exceeded one hundred per square mile, but in 1929–30 the coveys were few enough and far enough apart to be identified and observed separately. If a covey of quail were truly resident, it usually could be located at any time within a quarter-mile of its customary headquarters. (In one exceptional instance the trail of an isolated covey was followed over a mile outside of its territory and then back again.)

By midwinter 1929–30, my outdoor exercise and counting and writing of field notes established that nearly all of some three hundred quail starting the winter on my observational areas were still alive.

By the end of the winter only about 180 were alive and present within the boundaries of these areas. Not all of this decline represented mortality. At least thirty-four birds survived the winter after moving out of the observational area. The actual wintering mortality figured out at about eighty quail on the 7,400 acres.

The most obvious fact about this mortality was that it involved very few quail that were in good physical condition. During a two-day snow storm, a wintering marsh hawk was known to have caught three quail feeding in a cornfield. A fat quail made the mistake of sitting on a steaming manure pile when the air temperature was eighteen degrees below zero Fahrenheit; its feathers became saturated with moisture and, soon after flying away from the manure pile, it chilled and died. But there was no doubt about it; the quail that fell victim to either predation or freezing cold were characteristically birds that had first lost a fourth or more of their body weight from starvation.

On the observational areas events followed what came

to be recognized as predictable sequences. The quail coveys that had access to an abundant supply of nutritious weed seeds (seeds of pigeon-grass, hemp, smartweed, or lesser ragweed), the grains of cultivation (especially corn and soybeans), or native foods (such as squirrel-opened acorns) got along all right. A well-situated covey of twenty to thirty birds might lose one or two during the winter—or perhaps not any at all. Coveys might not lose any members even when living in places where hawks could be seen every day, owls could be heard hooting every night, and foxes would lay down their tracks either in daytime or nighttime. At the Prairie du Sac area, which had the most uniformly favorable wintering conditions for quail observed in 1929–30, the survival figure was 112 out of 121.

Where the food was inferior or in short supply a snowfall could quickly mean hungry quail. They might do some frantic ranging over the whitened countryside. They might leave their accustomed coverts and later come back. Or, they might not come back. Or, they might not do any special moving at all, except perhaps within a quarter-mile radius, and try to make out where they were.

Hungry quail might pick up a few acorn fragments or dropped corn under the squirrel perches, or glean amid the sparse ragweed growths sticking out of the snow, or work around in bean fields or corn stubble, finding what they could. Growing hungrier, they might peck at the small seeds of pigweed and lambsquarter, and stuff their crops with rose and sumac fruits, dried wild grapes, sweet clover, and black locust seeds. When I came to recognize this desperation behavior, the weathered owl pellet from the previous winter, with its mixture of quail bones and gizzard contents of sweet clover and locust seeds, made sense.

After a week or two of hunger, some of the quail would show weakness in flight. That is to say their flight might show a trace of "flutteriness" instead of the tense explosive quality of strong flight that reminds one of a steel spring released or a gong struck in cold air. I could not always be sure that I recognized weakness in flight, for

I have appraised flying birds as weak when they were not weak and failed to recognize the weakness of birds that were within a day or two of death. As a rule, the symptoms of weakness were recognizable.

Next, not long after "flutteriness" would be showing up in a covey's flight, I might find bunched quail feathers on the snow or wind-drifted feathers away from a fence post or some other feeding place of a flesh-eater. If I reached the scene early enough, I might find a frozen quail on a night roost, its breast profile sharp and its legs extended straight out. There might be a place where another quail ran over the snow leaving the wing marks of a long take-off, or a place where it flapped its wings without

BOBWHITE QUAIL

being able to rise. The trail might end at a spot marked by quail feathers, blood drops, and spread-out wing impressions of a redtailed hawk, and a redtail might fly screaming from its perching tree.

To learn more about how such a relatively clumsy hawk as a redtail could catch a quail, I would pursue an occasional weak member of a covey on foot. The weak bird might have in it a flight of 150 yards, or only one hundred yards or seventy-five. On the second flush, it might fly fifty yards; on the third flush, fifteen. It might attempt again to get into the air before flapping on the snow, as I ran up to catch it by hand. The demonstration would be complete. Any bird so helpless that I could catch it by hand would not stand much chance if pursued in the open by a wild enemy. If it could reach a mat of creeping juniper or a hole in the ground, it still might not have to let itself be caught by hawk or by man. It might have another day of life left.

With weakness so far advanced, a starving quail would not stand much chance of surviving if it were not pursued by anything predatory—not as long as a weather crisis continued, and perhaps not even if the snow melted and the bird fed well once more. The impartial cold could seek out the weak ones in cover too thick for hawk or owl or fox to hunt through. Let a cold snap come along, and emaciated quail would lie dead on roosts wherever quail were starving.

The starving coveys usually did not lose all of their members to hunger, cold, or predators before they found sufficient food again or the weather moderated. Covey remnants might make their way to human dwellings to feed perhaps among the poultry and livestock of a farmyard, watching out for dogs and cats as they fed. Sometimes and sometimes not, hunger-tamed quail would spend the rest of the winter about a farmyard. Sometimes, the last few birds of a desperate covey would join a better-situated group, sometimes splitting off from time to time into their own little subgroup.

Two neighboring coveys, each having eighteen birds when first observed in midwinter, provided an instructive contrast. One of the coveys was well fed and wintered without known loss, despite the fact that the favorite lookout tree of a redtailed hawk was about two hundred yards from the place where the quail fed in an open field. The other covey, starving, lost seven birds between January 25 and February 3, four more by February 12, at which time the remaining seven were plainly weak. The last five birds had joined the secure covey of eighteen by March 3, after which the combined covey lost one bird by March 27.

With the melting of the snow in late February, the hunger crisis was relieved for most of the quail on the southern Wisconsin observational areas. Mortality from all causes virtually ceased for the rest of the period that the fortunes of individual coveys could be followed.

My first winter of intensive study of the bobwhite quail thus furnished me with some nice, convenient, comfortable generalizations. These could be regarded as answering some of the practical questions that my fellowship money was in part contributed to answer. It looked as if, in northern quail management, the big answer to both winter-killing and predation was food—plenty of good food in places where the birds could get it.

THE NEXT WINTER, 1930–31, was one of the mildest on record for southern Wisconsin. Food resources were generally excellent in those places that were at all suitable for quail. The setup seemed ideal for testing the concept that well-fed quail should get along splendidly. That, in the main, is what they did.

Wintering losses for 510 quail on all my areas were recorded as forty-one. At Prairie du Sac, the loss was twenty-one from a total of 257 birds. The heaviest of all observed losses was nine birds out of an original sixty-seven on a 200-acre tract; on another area in the same neighborhood, forty-seven birds wintered on 160 acres without a single loss, even though a redtailed hawk was around all winter and sometimes perched within one hundred yards of the place most regularly frequented by the quail. One square-mile area wintered thirty-two birds with only one loss up to the last census on February 8, despite the presence of the heaviest predator population on any of the observational areas.

Mortality of about ten of the forty-one birds lost was charged to illegal shooting, and two more quail were taken as scientific specimens. Of the twenty-nine dying or disappearing from "natural" causes, six were known or suspected victims of Cooper's hawks, and four were horned owl victims. (Four additional victims were brought to a horned owl nest after the last satisfactory quail census.)

The winter was exceptional for its numbers of wintering Cooper's hawks, and these hawks occurred now and then on at least five of the seven regularly observed study areas. They were the most spectacular raiders and those most feared by the quail. However, after sacrifice of a bird or two while becoming educated to the special dangers of Cooper's hawks—or even without any loss—a covey of quail would become too "hawk-wise" to afford profitable hunting, and the Cooper's hawk would feed on some other prey or move on. The winter was also one during which horned owls, redtailed hawks, and gray foxes were present in what turned out to be about average abundance on those particular tracts of land.

So far in the quail investigations, at the end of my second winter, I could still stand by my generalizations from the year before. Well-fed quail wintering in the kind of environment that quail lived in were not absolutely secure from predatory enemies. Neither did they suffer severe losses. They had to be alert as well as physically fit to escape formidable enemies. Danger-tempered quail were wonderful birds and worthy of their evolution.

THE NEXT WINTER, until March, was as snowless, if not quite as mild, as that of 1930–31. In March, heavy snows resulted in a severe crisis for many quail coveys after one might reasonably have expected the winter to have been over. The dying of quail when up to two feet of snow covered the ground for two weeks fitted in with what I had learned in my first winter of study. It fitted in with

Gastrow's account of the hard and deadly winter the year before my study began.

A 400-acre area put under regular observation for the first time during that third winter of study was the site of a local cataclysm for the quail during the March weather crisis. Six coveys, totaling ninety birds as of about New Year's, had lost only a few birds up to the time of the heavy March snowfall, but by March 20 the local population was down to fifteen weak birds. A seventh covey wintering on the same area escaped the effect of the crisis by moving into a farmyard.

Away from Prairie du Sac, of approximately one hundred quail comprising the eight coveys subject to the severest starvation losses in March, fewer than one-fourth of the birds survived, and most of those barely made it. Up to the March crisis only about 3 per cent of those entering the winter were victims of wild predators.

So far, we can see little that differs much from losses observed during the two previous winters. But something different came from Prairie du Sac, the largest and best studied area, and the difference was that severe predation occurred that was not borne by hunger-weakened birds.

On the Prairie du Sac area, a population of four hundred quail entered the winter; about seventy were lost during the early and middle parts of the winter before the onset of any weather emergencies or food shortages. One covey lost twenty-four of the twenty-six birds present in mid-December, and the losses were largely from horned owl predation. Although four other coveys totaling sixty-five birds lived without any loss all winter in or near the nesting territory of the same pair of horned owls that almost annihilated the covey of twenty-six, the usual experience of the Prairie du Sac coveys was for each to lose from predation up to a half-dozen birds between November and midwinter. After midwinter, the quail seemed to live securely until the March emergency.

The almost-annihilated covey was notable for behavior suggesting that it did not have a suitable place to go. Its movements were rather satisfactorily traced nearly a mile and a half from the place where first recorded in late

October to the place where it permanently established its wintering territory about New Year's. The final wintering territory had an attractive food supply but terrain that was deficient in the sort of brushy cover that quail need for refuge from predatory enemies. During its adjustments of November and December, the covey passed by or through some much better tracts; and, to me, it seemed not to settle in these other places because these places were already occupied by quail having well-established property rights.

In some of the Prairie du Sac territories where coveys were suffering moderate losses from predation, the birds did not have access to food that was conveniently near their refuge cover. In other cases, I could see nothing wrong with the territories—they looked as if they could have taken care of more birds than they did—but the mild weather predation loss was still extraordinary compared with what I had seen during the previous two winters.

BEFORE THE NEXT WINTER I had left Wisconsin to go to Iowa, but Albert Gastrow continued the winter quail censusing at Prairie du Sac. I visited the area enough to see if the early winter loss patterns of the previous winter were being repeated. They were. The 406 quail entering the winter again were favorably situated with respect to weather and food. Again, the substantial mortality that the local quail coveys suffered through predation was borne mainly by strong, normal birds.

Most coveys lost from one to seven birds between December and April. The same tract of land where the wintering covey had been almost annihilated during my last year of study was the site of a similar happening in 1932–33. Again, this tract had excellent food resources but inferior refuge cover. It seemingly did not have what quail required for getting through a winter. As before, horned owls were the immediate agency of the mortality, though the covey territory was ranged by one red and four gray foxes in mid-December.

A high gray fox population practically never frequented three wintering territories of the quail, so the field data were examined to see if these quail got along any better than did the quail living where the foxes hunted. Loss rates of the quail on the foxless tracts turned out to be higher than on the fox-occupied tracts. These data should not be construed as meaning that gray foxes do not get quail or that quail losses through predation should be charged as a matter of course to horned owls, Cooper's hawks, or to any other predatory species frequenting an area. The loss rates suffered by the quail of foxless and fox-occupied tracts fit into another kind of picture, the outlines of which were just beginning to take form at the end of this fourth winter of intensive study.

A MOST SUGGESTIVE FACT coming out of the field data was that the survival figure of 339 for the mild winter of 1932–33 at Prairie du Sac was as close as it was to a figure of approximately 330 that could have been expected for

GREY FOX

1931–32 if the latter winter had not been terminated by
the weather emergency in March. It would seem that
somewhere around 330 to 340 bobwhite quail might represent close to an upper limit that the area in its existing
condition was able to accommodate even in a winter when
the quail had no starvation crises.

It looked to me as though some sort of threshold of
security existed. As long as the wintering population remained below a certain level, predation losses uncompli-
cated by weather emergencies were rather low and uniform, representing about the rates expected if a hawk, owl,
or fox managed to pick off one or two unlucky or "unedu-
cated" birds from a covey in the course of a winter. When
the population exceeded the level of about 330 birds, it
could draw quite severe predation as long as many birds
remained in excess of that level. But, when the population
had been reduced to the vicinity of 330 (as had occurred
by late winter, 1931–32, before the onset of the March
blizzard), it seemed to be fairly (not entirely) safe from the
local predators.

With this lead from Prairie du Sac in front of me, I
decided to examine closely the winter-by-winter case histories of the quail coveys or groups of coveys on my major
observational areas.

When field data were transferred to maps, it usually
could be seen that certain tracts were somewhat the equivalent of islands. Quail coveys or groups of coveys tended
to spend essentially all of their time for the duration of
the winter in their respective home tracts, though, within
the boundaries of those tracts, the resident coveys might
do much moving, combining, splitting up, and recombin-
ing. Both the smaller and the larger tracts, but especially
the larger, could show a remarkable uniformity in numbers of quail that they wintered. The winter survival for
a small tract might be seventeen birds, whether seventeen
or twenty-one or twenty-three started the winter; the combined group occupying a large tract might take good care
of itself under mild weather conditions at the level of
about sixty.

Not all of the case histories showed such uniformity

in numbers of birds wintering. Some of the late-winter population levels varied greatly from year to year, but the detailed field data generally could explain what happened whenever the survival figures for a tract were either peculiarly high or peculiarly low.

If the figures were peculiarly low, the usual explanation—other than a starvation emergency—was that a covey simply moved elsewhere. It might leave for reasons apparent only to the quail themselves or because someone cleared away the brushy cover of a favorite retreat or removed from a given field the last of the food (such as corn shocks) on which the birds were dependent. Other local adjustments might be in response to massing by the introduced ring-necked pheasants, heavy pasturing by livestock, destruction of food or cover by fire, or extreme and repeated disturbance by enemies including dogs and man.

Less commonly, the survival figures might be higher than expected for a given tract. As restless or evicted quail moved out of some parts of the study area, they might reappear somewhere, perhaps only briefly before moving on again. If these newcomers raised the number of quail in a wintering territory substantially above the number that could live there securely, the rise in predation rate could be spectacular. Then, when the excess birds were killed off or departed, the predation there would virtually cease. Sometimes, spring would come or the last accurate census would be made before the predators again trimmed back a temporarily out-of-balance population to the local threshold level; but evidence might still be found of continued responsiveness of predators to the vulnerability of the quail.

While considering the apparent threshold values of tracts of land for wintering quail under favorable climatic conditions and the usual fate of quail that were present in numbers exceeding those thresholds, I also thought much about the predators themselves. What, if any, were the changes in numbers or activities of the predators preying upon the quail? What, if any, were the changes in population status of prey animals other than the quail?

In 1929–30, most predators that could have preyed

upon quail were scarce at Prairie due Sac—probably not more than a pair of horned owls, a pair of gray foxes, and three redtailed hawks wintered on the whole study area. But, thereafter, plenty of formidable predators frequented the place: There were four horned owls, four redtails, and about sixteen gray foxes during the light-predation season of 1930–31; and Cooper's hawks—the most dreaded predatory enemies that the quail usually had—were more numerous that winter than they were in any other winter of the study.

Among the hawk, owl, and fox prey other than quail, meadow mice were conspicuously abundant the first winter of the study, then rather scarce for the next two winters, and moderately abundant again by the fourth. No estimates were made as to abundance of deer mice at the beginning of the study when all mice were dominated by the meadow mice, but the deer mice then had two winters of moderate abundance followed by one of great abundance. Gastrow, thinking as a hunter, considered cottontail rabbits moderately abundant throughout all four winters.

So far, in viewing the data from the Prairie du Sac area as a whole, I could see that neither the predator populations capable of preying upon quail when they had opportunities nor the total quantity of prospective mouse and rabbit prey differed very much from the winter of 1930–31 through that of 1932–33. During 1929–30, a sparse predator population gorged with meadow mice preyed upon a rather low quail population at about the same rate as a much heavier predator population preyed upon twice as large a quail population during 1930–31— and after a natural collapse of the meadow mouse population had almost eliminated this staple food from the diets of the local predators.

When I worked over the case histories for the individual covey ranges or territories, I had some basic facts impressed upon me. A three-covey group of forty-eight quail was persistently harried by Cooper's hawks, yet lost only one bird. A two-covey group of thirty-two did not lose a single bird from mid-December past mid-March, even though its members were frequently active within one hundred yards of a horned owl nest. Again and again, it could be seen that some of the most secure quail coveys on the area wintered right in the midst of the heaviest predator populations for weeks or months at a time. Yet a vulnerable covey off in a place frequented by relatively few predators might be whittled down, bird by bird, until the survivors reached a level at which they could take care of themselves, there or somewhere else.

In short, the severity of losses from predation suffered by a Prairie du Sac quail covey seemed to be linked with the essential vulnerability of the quail themselves far more than with variations in kinds and numbers of predators or with ups and downs of staple prey of the predators.

GASTROW SPENT an average of three days a week keeping track of the quail wintering on the Prairie du Sac area during 1933–34 and 1934–35, and I got back to Wisconsin to work with him several times during these winters. Each winter had its distinctive features, so far as the quail were concerned.

The first of these two winters was of moderate severity, resulting in no important losses from weather emergencies for the extraordinarily high quail population that entered the winter; but emergency conditions of a man-made sort—clearing of brushy cover from roadsides—did have drastic impacts on some wintering territories. I estimated (at the time and on the ground) that thirty to forty quail had been evicted by the de-brushing and without possibility of finding suitable quarters elsewhere on the area. If the quail thus evicted had not been evicted, their numbers added to the survival figure of 288 recorded for the area should have given a figure probably not much below 330, or about at the threshold suggested by the earlier data.

The next winter of 1934–35 was one of both emergency and non-emergency losses at Prairie du Sac. A population computed at 411 quail in mid-November, was down to 196 by late March. Losses chargeable to mortality on the area totaled 176, of which 115 represented predation. This predation rate was the highest yet recorded but can be explained by the case histories of the groups of quail wintering or trying to winter.

The weather emergencies resulted in the kind of starvation losses that could have been expected with ice or deep snow covering the food. The emergencies also caused frantic movements of hungry quail that intensified the state of crowding already existing in places that still had plenty of food. One familiar tract, which in previous years had demonstrated its capacity to winter slightly more than fifty quail during non-emergency seasons, had seventy-two starting the winter and fifty finishing; but, between November and April, newcomers had repeatedly raised the local population above the secure level for the tract. The season's mortality there was determined at fifty-four, or a greater number than the birds that successfully wintered. Whenever the top-heaviness of the local population would be relieved by death or exodus of enough birds, predation would virtually cease. Although predation by the horned owls upon vulnerable quail was spectacular, covey territories not seriously affected by food shortage wintered about as many quail in each as they had been doing in the other winters. Some 350 actually had been getting along fairly well during the first half of the winter before the starvation crisis became acute. On the basis of this evidence, it seems reasonable that a survival in excess of three hundred birds, or possibly in the vicinity of the 330-bird threshold level indicated by the earlier years of records, might have been expected if the winter had been mild.

During my last winter of visits to Prairie du Sac, 1935–36, the second half of December brought a period of deep snow and some cold weather. Of the quail population of 416 entering the winter, at least 329 remained alive and fairly well established by midwinter. It looked as if we might have expected, by the spring of 1936, a quail survival a little lower than but still not far from the 330-bird threshold level indicated by the data of the previous winters—if no further weather or hunger emergencies complicated matters for the quail. Then, intense cold (down to 34 degrees below zero, Fahrenheit) prevailed from late January through most of February. Blizzard followed blizzard, snow lay up to two feet deep, and only the exceptionally lucky covey had a chance. The spring census gave seventy quail left alive on the Prairie du Sac area, and no one who knew quail was surprised that the losses had been so severe.

At the end of my seventh winter studying quail populations, 1935–36, the data from Iowa as well as Wisconsin areas seemed to be fitting into categories.

Each observational area that was large enough to include the places over which the winter-resident quail would be likely to range seemed to have its own threshold of security for the quail. Such thresholds seemed to be quite definite, with numerical values varying greatly with the area. Some thresholds seemed as high as around three hundred quail per square mile; others as low as only a dozen or so per square mile; and still others were apparently at zero level, insufficient to allow safe living for any quail, irrespective of how open the winter.

Fair evidence had also accumulated to indicate that the introduced ring-necked pheasants could substitute for quail on a bird-for-bird basis in the balancing that the threshold phenomena implied. Where wintering coverts were well-filled with quail *and* pheasants, more pheasants apparently could mean fewer quail—and not necessarily because the pheasants drove out the quail or ate up their food or did anything else so obvious. There might not even be withdrawal of quail from parts of an area occupied by the pheasants. Both species might feed together. Occasionally, as after ice storms, the quail might follow the pheasants to take advantage of the buried food that the more powerful pheasants exposed by pecking or scratching. But, if quail and pheasants together comprised a population of birds exceeding the threshold level holding for the quail, something tragic had ways of befalling birds that remained present above that threshold level.

Because of the tremendous local and annual differences in predator populations, and in populations of mice, rabbits, and other staple prey, I could not see that these

differences had any important bearing upon the number
of quail that could survive on an area under favorable
wintering conditions.

Under unfavorable wintering conditions, as when
the quail were weak enough to be easily caught by predators, they often died of cold instead of predation. Of
course, it could happen that attentions of persistent predators might aggravate a hunger or storm crisis for the quail,
but I had great difficulty in finding instances where this
sort of thing could have made any real difference in the
survival of wintering coveys.

The factors that really seemed to govern the numbers
of quail alive in the spring were—in addition to the presence of quail in the first place—the weather, the nature of
the environment available to the quail, and the psychology
of the quail in relation to the problems and resources they
had to live with. The predation that wintering quail suffered then seemed to be more or less incidental. Quail
populations above the threshold level for an area could be
vulnerable to predation, from few predators or many predators, as long as such a state of overpopulation continued
to exist. Quail populations at or below such threshold
levels generally wintered with slight loss from predation—
even when high populations of formidable predators were
present—unless some emergency greatly complicated life
for them.

Another generalization seemed valid on the basis of
especially the fall and spring census data from Prairie du
Sac: The percentages of gain shown by each year's quail
population from spring to the following fall tended to
conform to a pattern. The higher the spring population,
the lower would be the rate of gain shown by the fall figures, and *vice versa*. What this really did was to reflect a
tendency of the fall population to level off at or a little
over the four hundred mark. For example, a spring population of 196 birds in 1935 was followed by a gain of 112
per cent to bring the fall population up to 416; and a
spring population of 339 in 1933 required a gain of only
28 per cent to bring the fall population up to 433.

Some distinctions should be made in explaining the

nature of these rates of annual gain. It is not implied in the least that the birds of the fall populations were exclusively, or even largely, the same individual quail and the descendants of the same quail present on the area in the spring. It was obvious from several types of evidence that many of the quail wintering at Prairie du Sac could be expected to leave the area during the breeding months, and that many strange birds came in from surrounding areas during the period of fall population adjustments, the so-called "fall shuffle."

What the pattern in the rates of gain between spring and fall did signify was to a considerable extent a social phenomenon. The pattern was being maintained despite local variations in numbers of quail present at the beginning of the breeding season, despite variations in nesting success of the quail, and despite variations in predator populations. By late fall, after so much of the greenery and abundant cover of summer had dried up or thinned out or disappeared, the quail populations seemed determined by the birds' own adjustments both to their fellows and to the environment available to them.

6

MORE ABOUT PREDATION
AND THE BOBWHITE QUAIL

BY 1936, THE FINDINGS FROM seven winters of studies of southern Wisconsin quail were in reasonably good agreement with the findings from four winters on Iowa areas. I had reason to believe that some questions as to predation upon the northern bobwhite quail were settled enough to stay settled. At any rate, the population levels commonly maintained by the quail in both states seemed to have little or no connection with observed fluctuations in kinds and numbers of wild predators or with fluctuations of the staple rodent or rabbit foods of these predators.

It did not seem to make much difference what happened to vulnerable parts of quail populations so long as they were vulnerable. Sooner or later, the biological surpluses were eliminated by something, most likely by horned owls. Sooner or later, the direct or indirect role of quail to quail antagonism showed through the confusion of details, as when socially unassimilated quail might be forced into uninhabitable environment or into dangerous ways of life. There might be a "battle royal" between entire coveys in the fall, with some questions about property rights presumably being settled as a result.

SOME OF THE WISCONSIN and Iowa findings on quail and their predatory enemies were much at variance with

87

views held by sportsmen, gamekeepers, and professional biologists alike. They were at variance with the conventional version of the Balance of Nature and with a lot that the public considered only good common sense. For myself, I was not at all sure of the scientific propriety of extending the conclusions from these studies to areas outside of the north-central region—or, at the most, more than eastward to southern Ontario and New England. I knew from Stoddard's work that there were differences between predator-prey relationships in the northern and southern parts of the bobwhite's geographic range.

In the Southeast of Stoddard's investigations, the predatory mammals and birds were no more formidable as quail enemies and they also tended to be less abundant than their counterparts in the north-central study areas. Yet some of the predator pressure drawn by southern quail seemed to have incomparably greater depressive effect on their populations.

Stoddard and I thought about and discussed the subject of why my quail populations could follow their own courses with such a high degree of independence of local changes in the predator populations while his did not. It was true that some of the southern quail preserves had much higher quail populations than were usually to be found toward the northern extreme of quail range; hence they might have the greater numbers of vulnerable quail to be targets for predation. The most convincing explanation, however, seemed to be that north-central predators generally had such an abundance of staple prey to choose from in the rabbits, several species of mice, and the large insects of summer that they rarely experienced any real hunger pinch. Consequently, they took quail mainly when the quail were in a sufficiently bad way as to be easily catchable.

In the Southeast, the main staple food of potential quail enemies was the cotton rat. When southern cotton rats were abundant, the predators dependent upon them got along well, but when cotton rats became scarce—as happened from natural causes every few years—the predators might be forced really to work for a living. At such times, relatively minor but desperate predator populations might, through intensified campaigning, exert disproportionate hunting pressure upon quail that otherwise would not be especially preyed upon. Something of this sort also seemed a possible explanation for the severity of predation said to be suffered by quail of desert regions at times when ecological stringencies meant shortages of staple prey for local predators.

Among the unanswered questions still troubling me after seven winters' work were those relating to the mechanism of balancing and counterbalancing that underlay the thresholds of security. What was such a mechanism that could result in so much uniformity in numbers of quail that could be accommodated by a given area, despite big variations in local predator populations and despite some astounding year-to-year variations in food and refuge cover in places where the quail coveys wintered? Just how could it function?

Clearly, the uniformities that could be shown by winter survival figures did not reflect great uniformity in amounts of food and cover available to the quail. There had to be sufficient food and cover to make a tract of land habitable for them; but past a certain point, it did not seem to make a great deal of difference how much food and cover might be present. A large patch of woodland brush sufficient—so one might think—to give concealment or mechanical protection to hundreds of quail could lie next to a corncrib having sufficient food for thousands. But the maximum number of quail that might be expected to try to winter there, even at times of much desperate adjusting in the neighborhood, might perhaps be two coveys totaling about forty birds. If another source of food were made available for quail next to good cover two or three hundred yards away from the corncrib, perhaps an additional covey might station itself there.

Those of us who were working with quail in Wisconsin and Iowa tried experiments to raise artificially the threshold of security (or "carrying capacity," as we then called it) of a tract of land for wintering quail. It was hard to predict what would happen. Neither was it always easy to predict what would happen if the quality of the environment were lowered. Sometimes, favorite retreats of the quail in roadside or fence row thickets might be destroyed, roosting quarters might be burned over, food-bearing fields might be plowed or closely pastured by livestock or have their main sources of food removed. Sometimes, so much might happen that a quail territory might seem well on the way toward being wrecked—and the usual number of quail would winter there anyway. Then, deterioration might progress a little further, and almost suddenly it would seem, habitability for the quail might change.

In Iowa, my later quail studies were centered upon trying to find out what were the strategic features of a wintering territory that gave that territory whatever definiteness of threshold values it had. Patently, it had to link with quail psychology as well as with physical properties of the environment. In a few specific cases, I thought I had it figured out—it was this or that covert or this or that feeding area in relation to refuge that looked strategic. In most cases, I did not feel like concluding much of anything as to why this place maintained its uniform threshold and why that place did not when pronounced environmental changes occurred.

THE PERIOD OF COMFORTABLE generalizations in my quail studies terminated for the most part in 1936. Although I was to do but little more work on the Prairie du Sac area in person, Albert Gastrow continued the winter censusing there and sent me copies of his field notes. From the latter I learned that the November, 1936, quail population was unexpectedly low—145 birds, representing a rate of gain from the seventy-bird spring population of only about half of the rate expected on the basis of previous records. By the following April, the Prairie du Sac population was reduced to the still more unexpectedly low figure of forty-five.

It was expected that ice storms sealing off much of the food supply of the quail may have brought about emergency conditions and mortality from starvation. However, the early part of the winter was one of mild temperatures, and even before the ice storms or any climatic emergencies a decline of 25 birds took place—a very high rate of loss for such a low population. On the Iowa study areas, too, the quail all but disappeared from the three areas kept under close observation. Something about the wintering fortunes of both Wisconsin and Iowa quail looked very different from anything I had seen before.

I began to work over the Iowa and Wisconsin notes some more to see what might have been overlooked in my earlier summaries. Certain facts did seem to deserve closer study. One was that in 1935–36 many north-central quail died that, according to usual criteria, should have been fit enough and well-situated enough to have survived any of the cold weather occurring earlier in the studies. Losses of up to 80 per cent of the quail wintering on areas in both Iowa and Wisconsin were considered due not only to the freezing of starving birds but also, at the time, to birds being worn down by the prolonged intense cold. Even so, there seemed to be still something else. Although some quail survived far more severe weather in western South Dakota, where air temperatures got down to 58 degrees below zero Fahrenheit, others were known to have succumbed in Wisconsin when in full flesh and before the onset of the severe weather.

Gastrow considered the cottontail rabbits only about a third as numerous in 1936–37 as they had been during the previous seven winters. Maybe the shortage of rabbits combined with a still-abundant population of the predators that preyed upon them had something to do with the heavy quail losses. Maybe this was not the answer either.

Maybe the answer lay in factors that no one yet understood. The peculiar phenomena at Prairie du Sac (and on the Iowa quail areas, too) did coincide with the years of "cyclic low" for populations of the snowshoe hares and ruffed grouse of the "North Woods" parts of the north-central region—a conspicuous though little-understood type of fluctuation. This naturally led to questions as to whether the quail might be responding to basically the same influence that was depressing the hares and grouse, whatever that might be.

There are limits to what may thus be proved with respect to "cyclic" hypotheses, but the fact should not be ignored that peculiar things happened during 1936 and 1937 that were quite enough to disturb some of the generalizations I felt justified in making on the basis of the earlier data.

I KEPT INFORMED ABOUT the further fortunes of the Prairie du Sac quail by correspondence for ten years more and continued my work on central Iowa quail populations as I had good opportunities until the early fifties. All together, the Wisconsin and Iowa quail investigations in which I have participated represented about two thousand man-days, covering two decades of chiefly winter field studies.

I shall not attempt here to trace the involved courses that my thinking took from the mid-thirties through the forties, but some of the more strategic of the later data may be discussed. It may be said that some of the field data obtained were among the most accurate and detailed of any of which I know. Three coveys, for example, lost forty-six birds, and thirty-seven of these were accounted for individually. Of one doomed covey of nineteen birds, seventeen were found dead of starvation, or of starvation and cold in combination, and another starving bird was taken by a horned owl.

The winter of 1940–41 was one of pronounced population adjustments on the Ames observational areas. An ice glaze covered the quail food for about a week, and, during this week, minimal temperatures were down to five degrees below zero. The particular quail that I studied did not find themselves up against a starvation emergency. They sheared away the unglazed underparts of corn husks. They followed pheasants that pecked through the ice to expose nubbins. They fed in farmyards with livestock.

Nevertheless, on one 1,500-acre area, the quail population declined from sixty-six to twenty-five between the middle of December and the melting of the ice in late January, and a fortnight later down to sixteen quail. Thereafter, the area remained almost quail-less for the rest of the winter. These quail had suffered little detected mortality on the area during the winter, though I cannot say what happened to them after they left. In conversation with farmers and through the most wearisome walking far outside of the regular study areas, I learned that quail were showing up in places in late winter where they had not been seen earlier. Some of these places did not look very habitable, and I suspected that the quail frequenting them might be suffering considerable predation.

Central Iowa weather conditions the next winter practically terminated the possibilities for accurate field studies before the studies could begin. In mid-December, I got a good count of 141 quail on 4,200 acres near Ames, but I did not succeed in censusing a long-studied one thousand-acre tract by the time a ferocious blizzard started on New Year's Day. Twenty inches of snow, thirty-five miles-per-hour winds, and air temperatures down to 24 degrees below zero for nearly two weeks all created a dramatic emergency. The deep snow made travel so difficult that I could cover only the area lying within walking distance of the University campus.

This area did contain a concentration of fifty-eight quail in one of the relatively accessible places, and I centered my studies on these birds for the duration of the emergency. By January 4, the local population had lost only one bird—that one still in juvenile plumage. On January 7, another immature bird was found dead, though in good flesh and with crop full of good food; still another quail had been eaten by a horned owl. The next day, eleven more dead quail were found—including four dying in starving condition on one night roost—and twenty-one seemed to represent the living remnant of the original fifty-eight. By January 13, after a thaw relieved the emergency, only nine quail were left, and these were frequenting a feeding station established by Ames sportsmen. Another part of the regularly visited area had forty-one quail as of mid-December, fourteen a month later.

Again, by spring, scattered coveys could be found wandering far from any places in which they would have been found in late fall and early winter. Most of these wandering coveys showed evidence of severe winter reduction, whether from hunger, weather, predation, or a combination of troubles.

The behavior patterns of the quail were well defined and seemed to be in response to food shortages caused by increasing use of mechanical corn pickers followed by heavy pasturing of the picked fields by livestock. In the fall, the adjusting quail populations would select the places having attractive brushy cover, and for a time they would maintain wintering territories there, and get along well until their food resources diminished or became less available as winter progressed. Thereafter, in their need, they would go almost anywhere, out in open fields and along brushless fence rows. Their numbers would dwindle away, or they would recombine their covey remnants to form larger coveys again, until spring took away the snow and brought mating time and new green growths and cover in which they could hide.

At Prairie du Sac, losses were unexpectedly high. During the early and mid-forties, four wintering populations averaging 250 lost about half; in 1945–46, a winter population of only 154 birds lost eighty-nine and the next year a population of 191 lost 105. Most of the mortality was from predation that was not associated with weather emergencies, but the losses were associated with unrest and local massing of the quail. It would seem as if the habitability of the area for quail had deteriorated spectacularly. But the winter of 1942–43, coming right in the midst of the series of depression winters, had a disarming normalcy about it—though I do not wish to impute too much normalcy to it.

During that winter, losses of 283 of 353 quail were singularly hard to separate into emergency and non-emergency categories. There were eight-foot snowdrifts on the area, and the snow was almost as deep in January and February, 1943, as it had been in the terrific winter of 1935–36. Some quail starved, and the depth of the snow may well have lowered the habitability of many coverts. The quail did suffer heavy predation, and night flushes of roosting quail by red foxes seemed to be important insofar as it resulted in individual birds alighting in exposed places—often on crusted snow—to chill and thus be easily caught by predators. However, the vulnerability of the quail to predation was evidently not nearly as great as during the other winters of the early and mid-forties; and the numbers of birds maintaining themselves fairly well until the weather became severe in midwinter suggest that upwards of 275 might have survived a mild winter.

Predator and staple prey populations at Prairie du Sac showed dramatic changes during the forties. Cottontail rabbits were exceedingly abundant early in the decade, and meadow mice reached a high abundance peak in 1942. Horned owl populations varied from seven to nine birds. Red foxes became exceedingly abundant by the mid-forties. During the winter of 1945–46, sixty-three red foxes were actually killed on the area.

If we considered only the heavy predator populations and the heavy losses of quail of the early and middle forties, there might seem to be a meaningful correlation, but I think that we should look more closely. Despite high predator populations, the quail population of 353 for 1942–43 showed a fair degree of security before the onset of emergency conditions in midwinter. Some of the severest quail losses of the other years of the forties were associated both with peak and moderately high populations of predators and both with abundance and a relative scarcity of rabbits and mice, those staple winter foods of the Prairie du Sac predators.

The quail data continue to suggest that something more influential than fluctuations in kinds and numbers of local predators and their staple foods must have operated and I find myself still thinking of thresholds—but thresholds with far more complexities in them than I had once thought. When the Prairie du Sac quail data for nearly two decades are plotted on coordinate paper, they suggest the operation of three thresholds of security.

One threshold applied mainly to the earlier years when the quail showed such a pronounced leveling off around the four hundred level and the rates of summer gain varied according to the extent that the habitat needed filling to reach that level.

Responsiveness of the population to the second threshold value was far more a phenomenon of the later years of the study, when predation rates were known to have been notably high in relation to the lower populations of birds wintering.

The third possible threshold value, applying to 1936 and 1945, represents very low rates of gain in relation to the spring populations.

The apparent switching back and forth from one threshold to another without any evident regularity or cause was the chief obstacle to my accepting any thesis of environmental changes underlying threshold changes. How could the threshold for 1942 jump to a high value after having been depressed in 1940 and 1941 and before being depressed again in 1943 and 1944? Granted that the Prairie du Sac quail coverts deteriorated conspicuously during the later years of the study—that much was plain from written descriptions and cover maps—why did the area's old threshold values apparently come back, if briefly, in 1942? What could happen to depress a threshold almost out of sight in 1936 and 1945, yet leave the area looking so much as it had during the years preceding and following both 1936 and 1945?

These latter two years coincided with the low population stages of the north-central region's ruffed grouse and snowshoe hares—the species best known for fluctuating according to an approximately ten-year periodicity. Perhaps if we knew more of what occurred at the times that the grouse and hares reached their low stages, we might know more of what happened to the quail. Perhaps we may temporarily dismiss the unknowns in the unthriving fortunes of the quail at Prairie du Sac in 1936 and 1945 by referring them to the other unknowns of what we call the "ten-year cycle." At any rate, I shall tentatively label these depression phenomena "cyclic" and come back to the subject shortly.

That would leave for our further consideration the gearshift effect of the changes between the high and intermediate thresholds of security. There was enough in this to confound anyone.

After I was beginning to feel hopeless about coming to any tenable conclusions, I had a chance to talk with Cyril Kabat who had done much careful work at Prairie du Sac after I had concluded my work there. He had observed that changes in year-to-year habitability of *certain* covey territories seemed to account for most of the threshold changes during the years of his own work on the area. For the weaker covey territories, habitability might hinge upon whether a farmer did or did not do something; whether he plowed or did not plow his grain stubble; whether he left out or took in his shocked corn.

It has been so long since I have seen the Prairie du Sac area in winter that I find it hard even to visualize, but Kabat's explanation seems consistent with the evidence and far more satisfying than anything I can think of.

RED FOX

IN 1946–47, I HAD on my mind the biological mystery of the "cyclic low," even though the near disappearance of quail in central Iowa seemed to be linked more with the weather crises of previous winters and even though the quail populations at Ames and those of southern Iowa and at Prairie du Sac did not seem to be in comparable stages of any cycle. The Prairie du Sac quail seemed to have passed their "cyclic low" a year earlier. Southern Iowa quail did not seem to have reached theirs—if they were going to. But, judging from the low population status of grouse, hares, pheasants, and much other wildlife in the north-central region, 1946–47 seemed chronologically to be about the right time to be looking for something unusual, for clues as to what might be operating.

Although I was no longer carrying on regular studies of quail, I was sufficiently familiar with about ten square miles of land in the vicinity of Ames—including, in part, an old quail study area—to know that there were only about two coveys living there. One covey was of nine birds, the other of fourteen. They lived a mile apart.

I decided to try to find out whether physiological changes might be reducing the ability of these birds to take care of themselves.

A decade before, at the time of a region-wide decline involving many kinds of game, Aldo Leopold found a half-dozen fat and well-fed quail helpless or dying in southern Wisconsin. One of these was enormous, weighing 250 grams, or nearly nine ounces, with crop full of corn—so weak as to be caught by hand after a flight of a few yards, yet without a detected sign of abnormality.

One member of my fourteen-bird covey flushed with the covey, then lost control of itself and fell to the ground after a thirty-five-yard flight. It flushed again and once more lost control, this time bouncing on the ground after a ten-foot flight. After it made another jump or two, I caught it, kept it alive for observation overnight, and took it to the Department of Veterinary Pathology at Iowa State University. It was found to be in excellent flesh, without apparent lesions or injuries except for bruises attributed to the falls.

Later, after preliminary consultations and arrangements with veterinarians and physiologists, I went out and shot five of the covey of nine for specimens and rushed them to the laboratory. We took blood samples, dissected glands, and otherwise did the best we could on the basis of our knowledge and equipment. We did not feel that we learned much.

AFTER THE THIRTIES many competent investigators worked on bobwhite quail populations in various places, but I shall not attempt here to review the resulting literature. These field studies had some things in common and others that were not. The role of environment in the life history and population ecology of the quail was affirmed and reaffirmed over and over again. As concerned predation, some local differences were found, bringing out additional facets of the drama of the eaters and the eaten.

In one place, the desperation of literally starving foxes seemed to be accompanied by unusual fox predation upon the area's quail. In another place, the severity of a drought limited the potentialities of the quail to compensate for nesting failures through renestings during the same breeding season—and thus gave losses of eggs through predatory egg eaters more population significance than when the quail had their normal breeding resilience.

In at least two other places, what made the difference between ordinary quail and predator relationships and an emergency type situation seemed to be nothing else than the artificial stocking of quail as an intended game management measure. The release of those strange quail upset the social order of the resident quail, the resulting turmoil drew the attention of opportunistic predators, and the artificially stocked areas came to have lower quail populations than they had before. I do not recall having seen this in print, but, in the course of one wildlife management conference, two investigators independently told me of observations on this sort of thing.

At that time, I had a few new observations of my own on social upsets in relation to vulnerability of quail to predation, made during the two winters 1948–49 and 1949–50 on my old central Iowa areas.

The task of obtaining in the late forties any population data from the Ames quail that could be used for comparisons with the threshold phenomena suggested by the data from the early thirties proved to be most discouraging. For one thing, I could not see much that was comparable in quail environment remaining on my old areas. Not only had Ames spread over some of my best-studied quail areas on the outskirts of town, but intensified farming practices had also thoroughly debrushed, plowed up, and pastured out most of the once-favored quail coverts elsewhere.

The few habitable places remaining for quail did have quail in them. I worked these places carefully, though the greater part of this last investment of daylight hours paid out in no very special results. As before, some quail starved, some tried to make out in exposed places and could not, some wandered, some got along well—the wintering fortunes of the local quail were about as they generally were for the region. Only the details of what happened to two neighboring coveys provided much that was worth recording.

In early winter, the above two coveys each had ten birds, living as distinct groups, with the usual headquarters of each covey being about one thousand yards apart. For convenience, one covey may be called the east covey and the other the west covey.

The east covey lived securely along a wooded hilltop bordered on its east side by a mechanically picked corn field and a field of soybeans on which the birds depended for food. From early December up to February 8, the covey lost no birds and had no trouble that it could not meet from a redtailed hawk having a favorite perching tree right at the edge of the woods and bean field.

The west covey had more attractive brushy refuge cover in a creek bottomland lying west of the wooded hilltop; but it had only a pastured cornfield in which to feed. At times when snow was on the ground, the main source of accessible quail food was on the tops of knolls from which the snow tended to blow off or melt. These bare ground feeding spots on the knolls were relatively far—up to 150

REDTAILED HAWK

yards—from the refuge cover, and the same redtail that perched over by the east covey also visited the west covey's territory.

About February 4, the redtail caught one of those too-wide-ranging, hungry quail of the west covey, and the earlier death of another quail probably had occurred through the agency of the same hawk. The west covey was eight rather than ten birds when it began a journey over toward the good feeding grounds of the east covey.

On February 6, the west covey was about three hundred yards east of its usual center of activity, and, from there, it moved to a large willow thicket west of and at the base of the wooded hill frequented by the east covey. The east covey came down to the willow thicket, and the two coveys were together in the afternoon, leaving tracks throughout the thicket. Toward late afternoon, both coveys flew eastward over the hill, the east covey of ten returning to its favorite place and the west covey going on to roost by itself in the cornfield east of the wooded hill.

On February 7, the east covey stayed where it belonged, while the west covey moved about in the same general neighborhood, at one time reaching a place fully a mile east of its own former retreat.

On the morning of February 8, the west covey moved in with the east covey. No evidence of fighting between the two coveys could be made out in the good tracking snow, and both coveys once rested together, tail-to-tail, as one bunch of eighteen; but there was running around and splitting up and "sign" indicating excited behavior. And, while the members of the two coveys were running all over the place, as if they did not know exactly what to do

with themselves or each other, the old redtail made three
passes that showed in the snow and got two quail by mid-
afternoon.

In one case, the redtail plunged into the side of a
gooseberry bush to get its quail, leaving several of its own
feathers on the bush. It made its unsuccessful attempt
through some fence row gooseberries and left feathers
stuck to thorns here, too. The second quail was caught by
surprise as it walked alone across an opening between two
gooseberry bushes. At three o'clock in the afternoon, the
hawk was circling over the woods. Evidence showed the
victims to be one bird from each covey.

Following the deadly experience of February 8, the
surviving seven of the west covey returned to their old
bottomland territory. There they suffered some more loss
because they had to search overly far into an open field for
food. The surviving nine of the east covey continued with
their former safe routine and lost no more birds up to the
end of the winter, the redtail watching over them as usual.
The east covey quail patently could keep their minds on
their job of staying alive when not unduly distracted by
visitors that did not belong.

THE PREDATION PICTURE APPLYING to north-central quail
that I think I see is still one of thresholds and emergencies. It looks to me as if the bobwhite quail's own
intolerance to its own kind—always to be considered in
relation to the setting provided by physical environment—
is the primary factor limiting its abundance in areas of my
familiarity. Predation accordingly operates more as a
secondary factor, of which the impacts upon the quail tend
not to vary either directly with kinds and numbers of
predators or with total numbers of quail present. Rather,
the severity of predation borne by a quail population
seems to depend more upon the numbers of quail present
in excess of the numbers that can be well accommodated at
a given time and place.

The case histories of wintering quail populations to
be extracted from Iowa and Wisconsin field notes show

about everything one could wish in variations. A few predators, even those of types that are not especially formidable, can exert very severe pressure upon either high or low quail populations if the quail are trying to winter at an extreme disadvantage. Conversely, either high or low quail populations can winter with slight if any loss from predation in areas having high populations of formidable predators if the quail are living in good environment and at population levels that the quail themselves find tolerable.

7

PHEASANTS AND GROUSE:
WHAT SOME STUDIES
SEEM TO SHOW

THE INTRODUCED RING-NECKED PHEASANT is at the same time the most abundant, the most popular, and the most thoroughly investigated game bird of north-central United States. Large populations occur in suitable places both eastward and westward from this region. And, everywhere in its recently acquired North American range, it is preyed upon by many kinds of predators, sometimes conspicuously.

In the north-central region of my familiarity, the examples of heaviest predation upon pheasants typically came from the areas having the heaviest populations of these birds. More than a fourth of the thousands of prey items examined from hundreds of Iowa red fox dens in the mid-thirties were pheasants. In the northwest part of the state where pheasants were particularly abundant, I counted remains of as many as thirty-four pheasants outside of a single fox den. A State Conservation Officer reported fifty-five outside of another den. Five other observed dens each had remains of between twenty-five and thirty pheasants outside. Recognized pheasant remains in fox droppings for this same period indicated, too, that foxes were eating pheasants.

It should be remembered, however, that foxes are known to exploit, sometimes very systematically, the pheasants that may be killed in great numbers by highway traffic. Foxes feed upon pheasants dying from weather emergencies and from various causes. They may bite off and swallow heads or feet of dead pheasants; bury, or carry to dens, or play with, or use as scent stations dead birds that they find—all in ways that look incriminating if possession or eating of pheasant remains is the only basis for judgment. Except for poultry, there is hardly any common fox food the traces of which may persist longer than pheasant remains as stomach or intestinal contents or as scattered feathers and bones.

The most spectacular proven predation suffered by Iowa pheasants at this time in the mid-thirties was by horned owls. In northwest Iowa "pheasant country" more than a fifth of the hundreds of horned owl pellets gathered in that period contained pheasant remains.

Proportions of pheasants in the diets of both foxes and horned owls ran particularly high in the spring of the year, and both these predators took pheasants in about the same sex ratios as existed for the general populations of pheasants. It therefore did not follow that either the gaudy colors and conspicuous antics of the cock pheasants or the closeness with which hens stayed on their nests made one sex or the other more vulnerable to enemies.

An abundance peak of pheasants in northwest Iowa meant a wintering density of sixty-five birds or more per square mile over large tracts of good range, and it is no wonder that they drew predation. But there is more to the predator-pheasant relationship than predators responding to an abundance of pheasants. Examples of relatively severe predation upon low populations of pheasants occupying marginal quality range prove that predation need not be in direct proportion to the number of the birds living in a given area. In central Iowa, pheasants showed up from time to time in horned owl diets, and remains of a half-dozen pheasants might be seen about a fox den in an area that wintered as few as ten pheasants or less per square mile.

So far as they go, the data on horned owl predation upon pheasants are reminiscent of horned owl predation upon quail with predation reflecting the security or insecurity of the pheasants within the environment. And it was apparent, from observations on the behavior of the pheasants, that increasing intolerance and restlessness of the birds with the onset of their breeding season must effectively lower the carrying capacity of an area for an adult population.

IN CONSIDERING THE POPULATION dynamics of the ring-necked pheasant, let us begin by turning back to the quail on the Prairie du Sac area. There the definiteness of certain population growth rates, security from predation within certain population limits suggested self-limiting forces within the quail population.

We have similar evidence of self-limiting forces for mixed populations of quail and pheasants on several north-central study areas. On these areas, the pheasant population, considered alone, did not conform to any clear pattern at all, and to a somewhat lesser extent, neither did the quail population from areas having substantial pheasant populations. Combined populations of pheasants and quail defined about the same patterns of gain (and loss) that the quail populations could have been expected to define in the absence of the pheasants. To the extent that the pheasants fitted into these patterns about as the quail did, with quail and pheasants seeming to substitute for each other in counterbalancing, there is evidence that the population dynamics of the two species have much in common.

On our principal central Iowa study area on which mixed populations of quail and pheasants were found to conform to the above type of patterns, horned owls and redtailed hawks maintained their breeding levels at approximately a pair of each species per two square miles throughout the period of study. Other predators—Cooper's and marsh hawks, barred owls, minks, and red foxes—varied greatly from one year to another. Occasionally something special such as a coyote, snowy owl, or goshawk might appear on the Ames areas.

(A goshawk might flush from the fresh body of a hen pheasant in an open fence row, and the speed of the hawk's flight might be chiefly demonstrated by the rapidity with which its body grew small in straightaway flight, its wings pumping with small-angle strokes. I should say that a goshawk could take a grown pheasant if any hawk could —though I have witnessed competent work on the part of a large Cooper's hawk, too.)

None of the variations in central Iowa predator populations linked with ups and downs of the quail or pheasant populations. The year of the highest rate of gain for the quail-pheasant combination was the year of probably the heaviest red fox population occurring during the quarter-century that I did intensive field work in the vicinity of Ames. Local abundances of mice and rabbits also showed great variation from year to year. Cottontail rabbits at Ames, as at Prairie du Sac, had declined sharply by 1936; but it is of some interest that at Ames their chief predatory enemy, the red fox, had all but disappeared before the rabbit decline.

There is fair evidence of self-limiting tendencies in pheasant populations, considered alone. Off the coast of Washington, A. S. Einarsen[13] studied an island population of pheasants that increased from a 1937 spring release of

HEN PHEASANT AND CHICKS

two cocks and six hens to a 1941 fall population of 1,540 birds. Although no predator control was carried on and the 397-acre island attracted many migrating birds of prey (including horned owls and Cooper's hawks), the growth curve of the pheasant population had no irregularities that seemed associated with predation. After the second year, the rates of gain showed the same type of falling off with increased breeding densities that the rates of gain for the north-central quail populations tended to show.

As I write this chapter, I have before me a paper by Joseph Péterfay on pheasant populations of Hungarian hunting grounds. These areas were subject to intensive predator control; but, even so, the population patterns of the pheasants resembled those on Einarsen's area. The Hungarian data showed automatic damping of rates of increase as breeding densities rose, a wide variety of mortality factors, and a conspicuous restlessness at times of high pheasant populations.

Hen pheasants, though satisfied with hatching out one brood of chicks during a breeding season, are ready renesters when their early clutches of eggs are lost through predation or accident. A three-year study by Frederick and Frances Hamerstrom[14] in northwest Iowa showed that 77 per cent of 445 regularly observed nests were failures, yet between 70 and 80 per cent of the hens were calculated to have finally brought off their broods for the season. This compensation nullified the population effects of a very large proportion of the nesting losses. In another three-year study, this one by Charles Shick[15] in Michigan, nesting losses were nearly 70 per cent, and an estimated 60 to 65 per cent of the hens were successful in hatching out their season's brood of chicks, their "quota" for the season.

Contemporaneous food habits studies of marsh hawks in the same general areas where the Hamerstroms carried on their pheasant studies showed that young pheasants were the most frequently taken by the marsh hawks of any bird species. Yet ten pheasant broods counted in the favorite hunting grounds of the marsh hawks averaged 6.2 young per brood at the average age of about six weeks, whereas counts of twenty-two broods from the same locality but away from places usually hunted over by marsh hawks averaged 5.1 young per brood at the average age of about eight weeks. Lack of correlation between the seasonal shrinkage in size of pheasant broods and the presence or absence of marsh hawks seems but another manifestation of counterbalancing trends.

The question as to how much the population phenomena of ring-necked pheasants may properly be called "cyclic" leads into some of the most baffling complexities. Even if we restrict our consideration to the pronounced and almost general decline of pheasants across northern United States in the mid-forties, we find no great agreement among authors as to explanations. Just about every conceivable variation in weather, agricultural practice, and predator pressure occurred on a region-wide scale between the "high" years of 1941–42 and a virtual collapse culminating in the "low" of 1946–47. Predators—especially foxes—got the blame from sporting groups in many midwest areas, but there were other areas where predators were scarce and on which the pheasants declined anyway.

An isolated pheasant population on ten thousand-acre Pelee Island, Ontario, built up to as high as five birds per acre in the mid-thirties and declined to about a fifth of that density by the mid-forties. In his intensive study there, Allen W. Stokes[16] found the low populations of predators responding to availability of pheasants but ruled out predation as an explanation for the pheasant fluctuations.

There can be little doubt that many kinds of animals do indeed eat pheasants whenever they have opportunities. My feeling has been for a long time that the ring-necked pheasant, as an exotic species in North America, may suffer disproportionately higher losses from predation than do native species that are better adjusted to native predators. Even so, I still know of no evidence suggesting predation as a factor genuinely limiting free-living wild pheasant populations over sizeable areas of land. In most North American regions offering suitable living conditions, the pheasant still seems to have what it needs, and something to spare, to determine its own abundance levels. This generalization might not cover fully a case such as a massive goshawk invasion during a hard winter, but I do not think it is misleading.

HUNGARIAN PARTRIDGES ARE BIRDS that may be substantially preyed upon by north-central predators having opportunities to do so. They were quite abundant in northwestern Iowa in the early thirties—though of lesser abundance than the pheasants—and drew predation accordingly. They comprised almost 2 per cent of the summer prey items recorded for the marsh hawks we studied, a similar percentage of the items at the fox dens, and were identified in 1 per cent of the fox droppings and 7 per cent of the horned owl pellets.

The population dynamics of the partridges not only show similarities to those of the quail and the pheasants, but some evidence exists that the partridges, the quail, and the pheasants may substitute for each other in natural counterbalancing. For the 2,400-acre Faville grove area studied by University of Wisconsin personnel from the mid-thirties to the early forties, spring-to-fall gains for the partridges, quail, and pheasants showed slight evidence of self-limiting patterns when the population figures for each species were considered separately. Combined, they showed the familiar patterns with rates of gain decreasing about as the spring populations of wild gallinaceous birds increased on the area. This reinforces the concept of a between-species equilibrium, extending the concept to cover a three-way competition instead of the two-way competition previously introduced.

I do not know how far I can go in saying that these partridges, quail, and pheasants exerted a mutually depressive influence on each other. Undoubtedly, each species adjusted to special features of the environment in its own ways, in accordance with its own racial adaptations. In all probability, little of the competition between these related species took such obvious forms as fighting—the fighting under such conditions more likely occurred between partridge and partridge, quail and quail, and pheasant and pheasant. I would put more emphasis upon the bloodless withdrawals and the different degrees of vulnerability that can influence the course of populations—that can determine in part what gets preyed upon by opportunistic predators.

THE FOOD HABITS STUDIES of predatory mammals and birds carried on in connection with the Wisconsin quail investigations brought out numerous instances of losses from predation suffered by rather sparse populations of ruffed grouse on the Prairie du Sac and neighboring areas. A barred owl pellet contained remains of what seemed to have been a grouse chick, and I once found a ruffed grouse in the nest of a redtailed hawk—a most unusual occurrence in my experience. Remains of ruffed grouse were found in stomachs and intestinal contents in two of 111 gray foxes. Occasionally, a scattering of feathers or a battered breast bone of a ruffed grouse would be found, perhaps with crow or dog or fox tracks about it but nothing to tell what had really happened except that a grouse had died.

Most detected predation upon ruffed grouse occurred through the agency of the great horned owl. Ruffed grouse remains were found in about 1 per cent of the horned owl pellets gathered from areas having resident populations of ruffed grouse, with some fair-sized lots containing remains in as high as 5 per cent. As in the case of the pheasants, predation rates upon the ruffed grouse tended to be higher in the spring, though horned owl predation upon wintering birds that apparently exceeded threshold levels was commonly noted.

Prairie du Sac furnished only marginal environment for the ruffed grouse. Up to the early forties, the average number of the grouse entering the winter was estimated at about twenty and the average number finishing at about seventeen. Horned owls were known to kill two or three during an average winter of the thirties, but no evidence of horned owl or any other predation upon the grouse would be noted in some winters—as when the grouse population entered the winter at a number below the average, as between fifteen and eighteen. And, as expected, the one winter of the thirties having the highest initial grouse population (an estimated thirty-three) was the winter of by far the heaviest owl pressure upon the grouse: the overall mortality of the wintering grouse was approximately 50 per cent.

No correlation was to be seen between numbers of horned owls on the Prairie du Sac area and the severity of the horned owl predation suffered by the grouse. Only the average number of six horned owls wintered when grouse losses were so severe. That was true also for the winter having the next highest loss rate for the decade, when a population of about twenty-five grouse was reduced to about seventeen. There were seven wintering horned owls during the winter of deadly severity for the quail, 1935–36, but the entire ruffed grouse population of about fifteen apparently wintered without loss.

Then the Prairie du Sac ruffed grouse increased and maintained themselves at substantially higher levels during the early and mid-forties. It could be that what might be called the carrying capacity of the Prairie du Sac range for the grouse improved in those years, even as predator populations reached their highest general levels for the period of study. Whatever happened, we had such population estimates as thirty-eight of fifty grouse wintering in 1942–43, with six horned owls present; thirty of forty-five grouse in 1944–45, with five horned owls; twenty-five of thirty in the next year, with nine horned owls; and forty-five of fifty in the year after that, with nine horned owls.

Of the latter winters in the Prairie du Sac series of records, the last was the one during which the grouse seemed most secure at a high level, yet the area not only had one of its two highest horned owl populations but also the peak fall population figure of about fifty red foxes. Although considerable variation in numbers of the horned owls and red foxes could occur between fall and spring— especially for a game species such as the red fox—there were plenty of predators around at any given time. The evidence appears plain that when the grouse found conditions favorable to their own increase and maintenance of a higher population level, they responded, the high populations of predators notwithstanding.

In considering the population fortunes of the Prairie du Sac grouse, I cannot quite discount the possibility that the fortunes of the other two wild gallinaceous species may have been in the equation somehow. Whether we consider the ruffed grouse, or the quail some more, or the pheasants, the ups and downs of none of these species seem to be associated with changes in numbers of predatory enemies in any convincing manner. For every instance in which it looks as if there may be a correlation, there are others in which it is apparent that the quail, the grouse, and the pheasant levels were independent of year-to-year changes in the predator populations of the area.

Skunks are eaters of grouse eggs as well as of quail eggs, and the grouse have far less nesting resilience than the quail. Horned owls and foxes are probably even more formidable grouse enemies than they are quail enemies— at any rate, a reasonable case might be made for such a thesis. Insofar as the grouse population virtually doubled during the years of the great increase of predators, the likelihood is strengthened that something more fundamental than changes in local predator populations must have been responsible for the changes in status of both the quail and the grouse.

The pheasant population at Prairie du Sac followed a pattern of increase similar to that of the ruffed grouse. The area's pheasants were not known to have gotten past a fifteen-bird winter level before 1941; then the early winter population was estimated at forty. Thereafter, the early winter estimates varied from thirty to thirty-five, except for fourteen in 1943.

The period of highest pheasant populations thus coincided in part with the period of the highest predator populations. If the ascending populations of predators could not more nearly keep down the really not-too-well-adjusted pheasants, it does not seem plausible that the increased numbers of predators could be the basic explanation for the decline of the native bobwhite quail.

Thinking of these wild gallinaceous birds at Prairie

du Sac, I am again reminded of how little we know about competition between closely related species. Could there have been, for example, any tendency for higher populations of the native ruffed grouse to substitute for the native quail, after the fashion that the introduced ring-necked pheasants apparently substituted for quail both at Prairie du Sac and at Ames? The real ascendancy of the grouse at Prairie du Sac did come mostly (not entirely) during the years when the status of the quail generally deteriorated; but the grouse were at least partially segregated into their own special environmental types. There could have been differential mortality of young or withdrawals of one species from coverts frequented by the other. Still, as concerns so many things, we cannot say that we know.

The most severe local predation upon ruffed grouse that I ever recorded for southern Wisconsin occurred in much better ruffed grouse range than at Prairie du Sac. This was north of Pine Bluff, where extensive stands of hardwoods stretched for miles along a series of valleys and hills. Three young grouse were brought to a Cooper's hawk nest within a space of five days, but a spring fire had destroyed most of the ground vegetation in a large tract surrounding the hawk nest. Other prey brought to this nest and to a neighboring Cooper's hawk nest during the period of study were five striped ground squirrels, a robin, a song sparrow, a bluejay, six flickers, seven redheaded woodpeckers, and seven unidentified small birds.

OF THE SEVERAL LONG-TERM investigations of ruffed grouse populations that public agencies have carried on in North America, I consider that two have been the most informative concerning predator-prey relationships. They are studies by the University of Minnesota and the State of New York. A third by the State of Wisconsin is very suggestive concerning the possible influence of heavy parasitism on vulnerability of ruffed grouse to predation.

The University of Minnesota research was begun by R. T. King.[17] He studied the ruffed grouse populations of an area of four square miles near Cloquet, in east-central Minnesota, for seven years beginning in 1930. As the grouse approached and attained what may be identified as the "cyclic high," their spring to fall population growth rates were the familiar ones: rates of gain diminished with increasing breeding densities. Their winter loss rates were the familiar ones: with increased population density, loss rates increased.

Then, with the onset of the apparent "cyclic low," both population growth patterns and winter loss patterns changed: growth rates were depressed and loss rates were increased.

The extent to which the Cloquet grouse conformed to patterns would seem to be of itself evidence that the population was not determined by local variations in predator populations, at least during the ascendancy and "cyclic high" years.

I had the opportunity to examine eighty-one horned owl pellets from the Cloquet area, representing winters and springs, 1932–34. Two of these pellets contained grouse remains for times when the peak fall populations leveled off at 640 by spring in both cases. This level of a bird per four acres appeared to have been a "saturation" density.

After King's study, William H. Marshall[18] reported the spring densities of the Cloquet grouse between 1940 and 1953. On the whole, the grouse populations were lower during the latter period than during King's time. Predatory birds on the Cloquet area included horned owls, goshawks, Cooper's hawks, and broadwinged hawks, all of which Marshall considered present in low numbers. Predatory mammals included coyotes, red foxes, bobcats, minks, and long-tailed weasels, of which the latter were the only ones ever to show any special abundance, even occasionally. Marshall did not consider that these predator populations could have varied sufficiently to account for the changes in the grouse populations.

Later, however, Robert L. Eng and Gordon W. Gullion[19] published a paper on goshawk predation upon the Cloquet grouse, in which they appraised this predation as being the most important single mortality factor for full-

GOSHAWK

grown grouse on the area. The losses through the agency of goshawks amounted to 30 per cent of the known losses of banded grouse and were heaviest in the spring when cover conditions were poorest. Over the four seasons, 1957–60, the goshawk toll was estimated at about ten grouse per square mile per year—or possibly more—for spring breeding populations of twenty-one to twenty-eight grouse per square mile.

These authors described a "circle of suppression" within a half-mile radius from the main goshawk nest and feeding area, but they were unable to measure how much the lower grouse populations within that circle were due to less satisfactory environment and how much to the effects of the goshawk predation. Drumming male grouse made up the largest segment of the victims, but rapid replacement by more males took place from surrounding areas, so that the removal of males by the goshawks did not seem to be any special hazard to reproduction of the grouse population. The probability was expressed that a large proportion of the ruffed grouse lost to the goshawks represented surplus birds.

The only other information on the Cloquet grouse of which I know related to an emergency situation. Gullion told me in late January, 1961, that the grouse were then greatly handicapped by a combination of cold weather and lack of blanketing snow on the ground and that they were suffering heavy losses.

In New York, where the Conservation Department carried on an exhaustive study of the ruffed grouse, the species showed a pronounced insecurity when its densities exceeded averages of one bird per four acres in the best grouse range. The final report of the New York grouse investigation was a 915-page monograph by Gardiner Bump, R. W. Darrow, F. C. Edminster, and W. F. Crissey[20] published in 1947. The lower of the annual breeding populations of the two principal study areas had a distinct tendency to show the greater relative increases of grouse between April and September.

Some of the exceptions to the above generalization seemed to line up with "cyclic" time schedules. Moreover, it may be seen from the data published by Edminster[21] in the late forties that the rates of winter loss from similar densities increased as the apparent "cyclic" time schedule advanced from "high" to "low."

The New York investigators carried on some experimental reduction of predators to find out whether the status of the grouse would be improved thereby. Lower nesting losses were recorded on the experimental areas than on the check areas where predators were left undisturbed, but juvenile mortality of the grouse remained about the same on both the experimental and check areas. At least during the years of high abundance of the grouse, stringent reduction of predators was not accompanied or followed by higher fall populations. The evidence suggested that reduction of predators might increase fall populations during the years of recovery from a "cyclic low," though, with grouse increasing anyway, justification for artificial reduction of predators in grouse management was considered doubtful.

Strong trends toward automatic adjustments and counterbalancing are indeed evident in the data from both the New York and the Minnesota investigations. If we compare the available data for these two investigations for the upgrade and peak years of the "ten-year cycle," we find that the rates of nest failures were very much higher in New York than in Minnesota and that the rates of loss of young birds were very much higher in Minnesota than in New York.

More can be said here concerning the "cyclic lows" of the ruffed grouse, insofar as this species is remarkable for its fluctuations and insofar as some authors consider predation to be the cause of the pronounced declines. One rather prevalent view is that another "classically cyclic" North Woods form, the snowshoe hare, builds up predator populations as it reaches its own population peaks; then, with the decline of the hares, the hungry predators turn to the grouse and force their population downward. I do not doubt that hungry predators may hunt with greater intensity than sated ones, but the hypothesis suffers from the fact that grouse declines may occur either before or after the hare declines, as well as contemporaneously.

Apart from the Cloquet case history reported by Eng and Gullion, some of the most conspicuous examples of predation upon ruffed grouse in north-central and northeastern United States have been by goshawks. In the present century, the most famous "goshawk winters" of these regions were those of 1906–07, 1916–18, and 1926–27. These dates line up well with the regional "low" phases of the "ten-year cycle" in the north-central region. My interpretation of the evidence is that the severity of goshawk predation upon the grouse may be a symptom of something being wrong with the grouse rather than a direct cause of the grouse decline. The grouse were often well on their way downward before any goshawks appeared.

Granted that the goshawks are formidable predators upon grouse, they still have their limitations in the sense that large Cooper's hawks or horned owls or other formi-

dable predators have theirs. I have observed, during the
years of "cyclic" increase, ruffed grouse living in fair abundance on a mountainous tract of south-central Montana
that was much hunted over by goshawks. While the Montana grouse were extremely wary of the goshawks and
might "freeze" for hours in the presence of Cooper's
hawks, they obviously could take care of themselves. I
remember watching a "freezing" grouse at the base of a
pine tree that would not fly even though I stood there
looking right down at it as it looked up at me—but in the
goshawk nest less than one hundred yards away I could
find no trace of grouse remains all summer.

Admittedly, I have not had the opportunities that I
might have wished to study goshawk predation upon
grouse but I have seen enough to suspect that the reported
instances of goshawks depopulating areas of the grouse
are not always explainable in the simpler terms of goshawks preying upon grouse at will.

THERE IS EVIDENCE SUGGESTING differential vulnerability of a particular species of grouse living in an area where
other species of grouse are also living. Frances Hamerstrom and Oswald Mattson[22] studied horned owl predation
upon prairie chickens and sharp-tailed grouse in central
Wisconsin. Of 571 pellets from the winter of 1936–37,
eleven contained remains of one or the other of these species of grouse. Including questionable identifications, the
ratio of prairie chicken to sharptail remains in the pellets
was seven to four, though the ratio of the prairie chickens
to the sharptails living in the neighborhood was one to
three.

It could, I suppose, be argued that the predation was
the reason the prairie chickens were fading, but there was
surely some more fundamental factor operating. Whenever I try to think this out, I keep coming back to the gist
of old conversations with the late Aldo Leopold, with the
Hamerstroms, and with other people in many other places.
I keep coming back to my own recollections of upland

game populations and upland game ranges. The following thesis best fits with the facts as I see them:

Since the white man settled north-central United States, the fortunes of several species of native grouse have shown profound changes with the passing of the decades. Prairie chickens reached tremendous abundances in response to an earlier stage of agricultural settlement, then faded as human land use became too intensive for them. In once-cultivated areas in process of being withdrawn from agriculture in the northern lake states, the prairie chickens again thrived for a time. Later they were supplanted by sharp-tailed grouse, which themselves faded as open fields returned to forest. Now, in our region the only native grouse that seems to have much of a future in sight is the ruffed grouse, which has increasingly large areas becoming suitable for it. The ecological balances will doubtless shift against the ruffed grouse in its turn.

Persons familiar with the living requirements and environmental preferences of the various species of native grouse can see where and how prairie chicken environment grades off into that of sharptail, sharptail into that of ruffed grouse, ruffed grouse into that of spruce grouse, a bird of primeval coniferous forest. One can also trace the changes from north woods grouse environments into those of the subarctic ptarmigans, or, southward, see where grouse environments grade off into those of bobwhite quail or wild turkeys.

All of these grouse and related gallinaceous birds can demonstrate their respective adjustments to first class environment by thriving there, thus demonstrating at least a minimum of ability to compete successfully with other species and to take care of themselves against predatory enemies. It is when we consider one or the other of them living or trying to live outside of superior environment that we get into the old questions of vulnerability to predation. When two species such as prairie chickens and sharptails (or such as sharptails and ruffed grouse, etc.) are closely associated, is the presence of one somehow disadvantageous to the other? When one species declines as the other maintains itself (or even gains), is one competing out the other, does the better-adapted make the less-adapted species less secure, or are the population changes directly and more or less exclusively a matter of environmental changes?

In recent decades, the introduction of the exotic pheasants and Hungarian partridges into the North American ranges of prairie chickens and sharptails has complicated the problem of trying to unravel the causes of the great deterioration of native prairie grouse populations that has occurred. In many cases, the native grouse were well on the way out before the exotics got a start; in others, the permanent decline of the grouse could very possibly be linked with the upsurge of the exotics, as for example in some formerly excellent prairie chicken range in eastern South Dakota. I cannot say how much the superimposing of hardy and prolific exotics upon the social structures of native grouse may have caused dislocations that made the grouse more vulnerable to predation than they otherwise might have been, but I have a suspicion that some phenomenon of that type may have occurred.

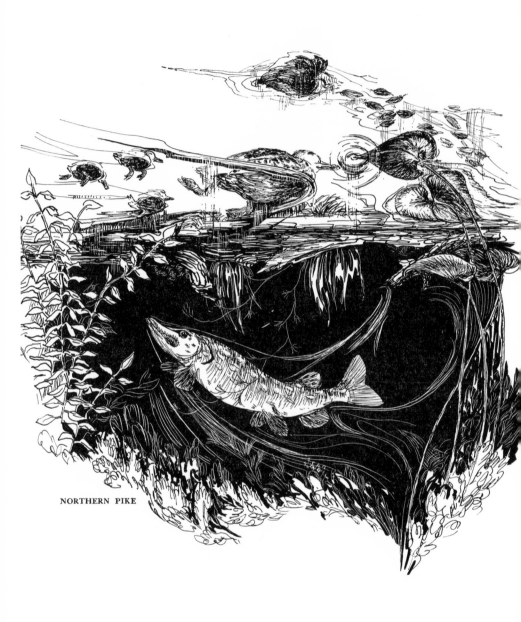

NORTHERN PIKE

8

WETLAND DRAMAS AND
PREDATION UPON WATERFOWL

PREDATION UPON WATERFOWL—upon ducks and coots in particular—can be dramatic. On the other hand, immense populations may live for weeks at a time with notable security. Thousands of ducks of numerous species may congregate about Iowa and Dakota wetlands before the hunting season starts and still almost nothing predatory can touch them. Even against the pressure of modern guns, wary mallards and pintails may adopt ways of life that give them a security as nearly absolute in proportion to numbers as wild populations of any species are likely to attain.

The predation that then occurs frequently is centered upon birds handicapped by injuries or weakness: We can see feathers and blood and bones and partly eaten carcasses where gunshot cripples or victims of lead poisoning were forced to remain near the last patches of open water at freeze-up or wandered helplessly over the ice as long as they stayed alive. Birds helpless from botulism may be preyed upon by hawks, crows, magpies, gulls, and carnivores, and no one should be surprised when lesser predators, even muskrats, take advantage of them when they can. Or, in spring, the return of wintry conditions may catch early migrants, and the birds may be weakened from starvation. Coots, especially, may starve on a dramatic scale when ice seals water, and snow deeply covers feeding grounds in adjacent pastures. Large hawks, the foxes, the coyotes, the minks are quick to respond to such increased availability of prey.

Of course, predation upon waterfowl suffering heavy mortality from any cause may grade off into what is not predation at all but merely scavenging upon the dead. A dead duck represents food for many hungry things, whether it was killed by teeth, talons, lead pellets, hunger, thirst, parasites, botulism toxin, or a telephone wire. On the marshes of central and northern Iowa, the bodies of coots wantonly shot by hunters and left lying where they fell may be a major dietary item throughout the winter for foxes, raccoons, and minks. Dead coots may be eaten out of the ice where imbedded; they may be dug out of the snow, sometimes out of snowdrifts many feet deep; they may be dragged over frozen surfaces or cached in land holes or in muskrat lodges or buried somewhere; or their dismembered parts may be scattered the same as may the bodies of prey killed by the eaters.

The great horned owl is not a very capable scavenger compared to creatures that follow their sensitive noses or drop down out of the sky to investigate stains or feathers. It is more likely to feed upon owl-killed prey, and, except for man, the horned owl is the only predator I have observed on my study areas to prey to any considerable extent upon migrating or resting waterfowl. That waterfowl concentrations may draw horned owl predation is illustrated by a collection of 158 spring pellets from an Iowa marsh: there were remains of ducks in twenty-four, rails in twenty-three, coots in seventeen, and grebes in seven. One lot of twenty pellets from fall contained duck remains in nine. Nevertheless, it is often astonishing how little horned owls living on marsh islands may prey upon waterfowl, even at times of tremendous waterfowl abundance. During some springs and falls, up to ten thousand ducks covered the approximately 135 acres of our Goose Lake study area at one time; they fed or slept or spent leisurely weeks, their bodies appearing as dark lumps on the sunset waters and blending into the dusk. Yet the pellets of horned owls collected under roost trees on islands in the midst of the marsh might still contain little except remains of blackbirds or land prey. Or, the waterfowl that the owls did prey upon might run more to the grebes, even though the ducks greatly outnumbered them, and I was unable to explain why.

Sometimes I could get a fair idea as to why a given individual had been killed but more often I could not. I remember that the only evidence of predation I found about one loafing congregation of ducks in late summer was a freshly mink-killed mallard, still in good flesh but with several lead shot in its gizzard. A group of one snow and four blue geese hung around a northern Iowa marsh for weeks after the normal migration was over, and the birds grew particularly tame, coming right up to people. Of these unworldly ones, the snow goose and one of the blues ended up at a fox den in the neighborhood.

Other evidence can be suggestive, such as the data obtained by Sam Erlinge (with whom I worked in Sweden) on otter predation suffered by mallards wintering along a stream in southern Sweden. Between three hundred and four hundred mallards were present both early and late in the winter, and more otters frequented the stream in the latter part of the winter than in the earlier; yet, forty-seven of the 250 otter droppings from early winter contained mallard remains, compared to just five of about six hundred for late winter. It looked as if, after the elimination of shot-injured or ailing birds shortly after the first freeze-up, there really were not many left that the otters could catch.

Predation upon grown ducks by eagles and other formidable diurnal birds of prey does not conform to easy generalizations. When a peregrine falcon knocks a duck out of the air at the termination of a spectacular stoop, an observer might marvel at the speed, precision, and power displayed and perhaps forget that the peregrine, too, is only a bird having the limitations of living things. Nor can the formidable goshawk be expected to take prey, waterfowl or anything else, exactly as it may wish. There is an exceptional case history of a goshawk destroying most of a population of mallards nesting on an island in the city of Stockholm. In another part of Sweden, a very capable ornithologist saw goshawks attempting to catch ducks in the vicinities of four closely observed goshawk nests, but the ducks regularly escaped by flying close to steep stream banks.

Golden, bald, or the European sea eagles may all seem more or less ignored by massed populations of waterfowl, or, if one of the eagles flies over the water in its hunting, the prospective prey may not have much trouble keeping out of its way. But any of these eagles can prey upon waterfowl on occasion. Sometimes the predation can look as direct and simple as golden eagles seizing mallards in flight over a river where they are wintering; sometimes it may be bald or sea eagles hunting coastal zones and using a technique of forcing a duck on the water to dive until exhausted; or it may be a matter of eiders actually being taken off their nests. The Swedish and Finnish archipelagoes have been sites of considerable predation by sea eagles upon eiders, but the season of greatest observed mortality from the eagles also preceded a year of great mortality from parasitic thorn-headed worms. Thus, one may wonder whether the eider population already had suffered debility at the time of the heavy predation. On the Norwegian side of the Scandinavian Peninsula, sea birds—and predominantly eiders—comprised nearly half of over eight hundred vertebrate food items listed for sea eagles by Johan Willgohs.[23]

THE PATCH OF OPEN water out in the foot-thick lake ice shrinks some more, and new snow covers the blood and feathers and duck droppings along the rim. The snow may settle straight down or slant in or swirl in the gusty wind. Perhaps one sees a big white bird moving; perhaps one becomes aware more gradually of something different sitting on the snow or ice—and there is a snowy owl. To me, it is always rather a bird of mystery from mysterious places, and it is nothing I expect to see every winter about the wetlands where I work. Nor do I find it staying long, but while it stays it embodies natural drama. Not only is the owl big and strong but it is fast when it needs to be, and it hunts boldly in the open and takes what it can catch and handle. The pellets of snowy owls that I see out on the ice near the water holes have the colors of mallard feathers showing on exposed surfaces, but I cannot tell whether these were of sound birds or ailing or of birds found dead.

THE NESTING SEASON OF waterfowl naturally increases the vulnerability of the hens to some predation. At this time, relatively clumsy predators may catch hens at nests: for example, raccoons may climb up and reach into holes in stubs or artificial nest boxes after wood ducks. Even so, the raiding of duck nests by raccoons may perhaps have still more noteworthy aspects.

Since the forties, raccoons have reached tremendous abundance about prairie marshes that in earlier decades of the century had been virtually outside of the geographic range of the species. The question of whether the raccoons of these places might now be regarded in the sense of exotic invaders from the standpoint of their impacts upon nesting waterfowl is not easy to answer; but the thoroughness of their searching for duck nests may, in extreme cases, arouse doubts that many broods of ducklings will be reared in a breeding season, irrespective of renesting efforts.

Such widely differing egg-eaters as skunks, crows, and bull snakes have been observed to depredate very severely upon duck nests in north-central United States and the Prairie Provinces of Canada.

Ralph H. Imler's[24] study in the late thirties and early forties revealed nest losses from bull snakes as high as 42 per cent in the Nebraska Sand Hills. The two principal food items taken by bull snakes during the summer months were duck eggs and meadow mice. Artificial reduction of the bull snakes reduced to about half the losses of duck nests attributable to the local bull snakes.

Crows and striped skunks have been much publicized

as destroyers of duck eggs, and there should be no doubt that, given good opportunities, they can be. The crows may not only take advantage of poorly concealed clutches of eggs (including, especially, those exposed by mowing), but E. R. Kalmbach[25] sometimes found that nests that seemed to be best concealed from human eyes suffered the most severely. In some cases where crows were reduced in numbers on waterfowl breeding grounds of central North America, egg losses from other predators, notably skunks, increased. Following reduction of the skunks in their turn, increased losses from still other predators seemed to substitute in an at least partly compensatory manner. Some data showed similar total loss rates in different years despite great variations in proportions of nests lost through different agencies.

In the early forties, B. W. Cartwright,[26] a Canadian biologist with long experience in the game-rich Prairie Provinces, put forth the hypothesis that a light to moderate degree of predation upon egg clutches served as a biological safeguard for grouse and Hungarian partridges. Despite the usual dryness of late summer in central North America, I think that a similar safeguard would apply to some extent to waterfowl. This region is one of occasional deadly climatic emergencies for young birds, and a species that hatched out all of its young at the time of one of these emergencies could have its entire season's reproduction jeopardized. Most species of ducks do not attempt renesting during the same breeding season if they succeed in actually hatching a clutch of eggs, whatever may happen to the ducklings. Light to moderate nest predation followed by renesting would therefore tend to stagger the hatching dates and work against the likelihood of any one emergency becoming too cataclysmic for the season's young at a critical time of life.

Members of the dog family—red foxes, coyotes, and domestic dogs, in my own experience—take whatever good opportunities they have to depredate on duck nests. An occasional fox, coyote, or domestic dog may learn to specialize in doing this. When I think of the hundreds of northern Iowa nests we found for research purposes by means of a trained dog over a period of a few years in the thirties, I can readily imagine the destruction that a free-hunting individual might commit if it got started on such a way of life of its own accord.

The most extreme cases of dog family depredations upon duck nests of which I know are, however, those in which a fox or a coyote got out on an island covered with nests. The resulting havoc may be understandably conspicuous, though still not necessarily easy to appraise in terms of biological consequences. In one case about which I have good secondhand information, foxes reached a colony of nesting eiders, which responded by abandoning the island and reestablishing themselves on another neighboring and suitable island that the foxes could not reach.

It is quite to be expected that, aside from emergencies due to detrimental human activities or to flooding or extremes of weather, the great hazard to the breeding success of dense island-nesting populations of waterfowl would be concerted predation. Such populations may be susceptible to predation not only by members of the dog family but also by members of the weasel family, by raccoons, by crows, ravens, gulls, or by whatever dangerous or opportunistic predators could get out to them.

Some of the most informative data on crowding of waterfowl nests on islands or other especially attractive sites are from the Lower Souris National Wildlife Refuge in northwestern North Dakota. Gadwall Island, with an area of less than an acre, had in 1947 at least 160 nesting pairs of ducks, a hatching success of about 90 per cent of the nests, and a total production of about 1,350 young. Ding Island, of slightly smaller size, maintained a popula-

NESTING EIDERS

tion of about one hundred nesting pairs or more, 1949–55. M. C. Hammond and G. E. Mann[27] generalized that the absence of predation on Lower Souris islands led to concentrations at rates of twenty to eighty nests per acre regularly for islands averaging between three-tenths of an acre and an acre in size.

These concentrations could have their exaggerated social phenomena, including manifestations of stress after populations reached top-heavy levels. Concentrations could, indeed, be resultants of a number of factors, but the relative inaccessibility of the islands to predatory mammals and the high rates of reproductive success prevailing over periods of several years undoubtedly contributed to the build-ups noted. Then, when something really does go wrong, the consequences may be devastating.

Waterfowl populations may adjust to predatory dangers by restricting their nesting to steep cliffs or to trees beyond reach of egg-eating mammals, whereas, when undisturbed, they customarily nest on open or flat ground. Following long periods of relief from molestation, the same species may expand their nesting areas to include once-dangerous sites. Or, waterfowl may learn that they gain protection, as from crows, by nesting in the midst of certain gull colonies. These adjustments reflect differences in experience as well as innate behavior patterns and in totality add up to the great generality that Nature's way is any way that works, as long as it works.

THE FINNISH BIOLOGIST, Jukka Koskimies,[28] obtained very fine data on Nature's way of working from a study of velvet scoters in southern Finland's archipelagoes. Originally the velvet scoter was a species inhabiting small inland waters of the northern coniferous zone in Scandinavia, and its abundant nesting in the Baltic archipelagoes is of recent occurrence.

The young scoters are sensitive to the bad weather and sharply fluctuating water temperatures of the archipelagoes, whereas their hatching season is late and synchronized with relatively comfortable conditions at the inland lakes. Extremely loose bonds between parents and young may have little significance in rearing the young within the confines of a small lake, but, out in an archipelago, the possibilities of mortality from the straying of young may be much greater.

This straying, which sometimes results in large aggregates of young scoters of miscellaneous origins trooping behind lone females, may make them notably vulnerable to predation—especially by large gulls—during their more helpless growth stages. The net survival of young observed by Koskimies out in the archipelagoes tended to be very low—virtually no survival during the worst years. Such low net productivity of course nullifies the generally high rates of success that the nesting birds have in hatching out their clutches and the advantages of the longevity of the breeding adults and their high fidelity toward particular nesting islands. Only through yearly replenishment with birds from the outside can the velvet scoter populations be maintained at the levels that are more or less characteristic of the archipelagoes.

This may seem to be the sort of thing that theoretically could not hold up under natural selection. A population of scoters that is not maintained by its own productivity and is basically dependent upon overflow birds reared elsewhere may not be considered biologically efficient; but that may not be said to bother Nature unduly as long as the production surpluses exist somewhere to maintain the archipelago populations. A biological luxury needs no survival value as long as it remains within the ability of the species to withstand.

Predation upon young waterfowl may be both conspicuous and hard to appraise, even if we restrict our attention to the occurrence of the predation alone and do not try to appraise the population significance of such predation. For instance, it is difficult to determine to what extent northern pike and snapping turtles prey upon young waterfowl. For these two species, digestion of duck remains progresses slowly, and the snappers also do much feeding on carrion.

While the northern pike certainly can be a voracious

and formidable predator upon higher as well as lower vertebrates that are vulnerable to its attacks, one of the heaviest pike populations that I ever saw was present in one of the best of our waterfowl marshes of northwest Iowa. In the course of ordinary paddling of a canoe about the marsh, the deadly looking forms of the pike could be seen through quiet water almost wherever one cared to look—yet this was a summer of very high productivity of ducks, coots, and other surface-swimming waterfowl. Whether the lack of predation could be explained in terms of escape cover for the birds, their behavior, or the behavior of the pike, it was clear that heavy predation did not inevitably result just because the pike and the young waterfowl were both present.

In contrast, Victor E. F. Solman[29] calculated losses of ducklings from pike predation at about 10 per cent of the average annual duck production of the Saskatchewan Delta during the summers of 1940 and 1941. Most of the duckling victims were less than a week old, and the young of diving ducks seemed more vulnerable to the pike than the young of dabbling ducks. Of 2,658 specimens of pike of the size range that would be apt to prey upon waterfowl, at least twenty-three contained from one to four ducklings. In this wilderness area, crows and other waterfowl predators characteristic of Canadian agricultural lands were absent.

I have seen on Iowa marshes little evidence of predation by snapping turtles upon young marsh birds, despite populations of snappers that amounted to—in one outstandingly clear instance—tons per acre. Turtle predation upon waterfowl was not completely unknown on this marsh, but it seemed to be of very minor intensity, the tremendous turtle population notwithstanding. I seldom found anything except submerged plant material and small quantities of fish and crayfish remains in the stomachs and intestines of the snapping turtles that I examined.

The reputation of the snapping turtle as a waterfowl predator has its chief factual basis in work carried on in northeastern United States. Malcolm W. Coulter[30] studied Maine habitats in which both waterfowl and snapping turtles were abundant, and collected turtles for specimens only during the peak of the brood season for ducks. Of the 171 turtles examined, 157 had food in their alimentary tracts, and, of the latter, forty-two contained remains of a minimum of fifty-two birds, including twenty-five ducks. The duck species were about what one might expect for the Northeast in the late forties and early fifties: mostly black ducks and ringnecks and mostly young birds up to six weeks of age. A thirty-one-pound turtle had eaten five water birds (a ringneck, a goldeneye, and three pied-billed grebes), and a twenty-four-pounder had eaten two black ducks, an unidentified dabbling duck, and a grebe. Surface-feeding ducks were taken as turtle prey almost twice as frequently as divers.

Emergencies may, quite expectedly, predispose waterfowl to predation losses. Flightless ducklings or moulting adults out on drought-exposed mud flats may have little chance to escape in the event of discovery by a coyote or a large hawk or almost anything able to catch and handle them. But the handicaps of emergencies are not wholly a matter of once-mobile prey not being able to move fast enough or to reach refuge to escape enemies; drought conditions, for example, have been known to greatly increase the amount and the reproductive significance of waterfowl egg losses through predation.

John P. Rogers[31] obtained two years of data on the reproductive fortunes of lesser scaups on a square mile of pothole country in southwestern Manitoba. The square mile contained twenty potholes from one-half acre to twenty-five acres in size and totaling 135 acres. In 1957, when water levels were favorable, fifty-one pairs of scaups produced 225 young in a minimum of twenty-five broods. In the drought summer of 1958, when wide flats of exposed mud separated the emergent vegetation from what little water remained, sixty-five pairs were recorded for the study area, but these produced only twenty young in a total of three broods. Of twenty-six lesser scaup nests found on the area in 1958, one hatched and twenty-one were destroyed by predators, mostly mammalian. Little evidence of renesting was found in 1958, which, in combination with the greater vulnerability of nests in dried-out edge cover, would seem to explain the severe decline in production of the scaups.

PREDATION UPON DUCKS AND ducklings by the more active members of the weasel family—whether of large-sized members or small—deserves special mention. It is not strange that the stocky, methodical striped skunk, with its physiological need for sulphur, should be known as an egg plunderer though not much of a predator upon agile prey; but it has some wetland relatives that are among the most accomplished of predators.

Although the predatory skills of an otter are chiefly those of a fish catcher, it can and does sometimes prey rather heavily upon waterfowl. The otter is said to come up from below the surface of the water to seize a victim, but I have no firsthand information on how often this happens; my own observations suggest that it does much hunting by swimming or wading in marshy shallows overgrown with emergent vegetation. In any event, by far the highest representation of mallard remains that Sam Erlinge found in otter droppings of southern Sweden occurred between late May and late June, when newly hatched young were most available. One lot of 280 droppings for this period contained mallard remains in thirty-four, and, during summer and early autumn, otters might now and then feed upon a young duck or a moulting adult.

The true weasels of the genus *Mustela* may be avid killers of adult as well as young waterfowl when they have exceptional chances. A party of biologists visited one of the small Lower Souris islands one summer day in 1936 and found fifty-nine ducks and coots that had been killed by one or more stranded weasels. Subsequent observations at Lower Souris indicated that minks, if present, usually preyed heavily upon nesting ducks and ducklings.

My own observations on mink predation upon ducks and ducklings in northern United States suggest equally severe predation drawn by crowded nesting populations, regardless of whether the nesting and rearing were done on the mainland or on islands accessible to the minks.

Of the two most extreme cases that I have seen, one related to midsummer mink predation in 1948 along a stretch of shore zone of Lower Red Rock Lake, in south-central Montana. I do not recall having seen before or since quite such a concentration of ducklings as I saw then in and out from the Red Rock Lake shallows. I should say that upwards of twenty-five broods of small ducklings per acre frequented the fifty-yard margin along shore, and this density was rather uniformly distributed as far as I could see in both directions along the shore. They were there with their mothers, the broods of gadwalls and mallards and ruddies in particular, and about everything else of duck species belonging about western North American marshes. Up on shore from one place where I stood there was a mink den with four or five half-grown minks flitting in and out of it. The approximately three hundred mink droppings that I examined contained scarcely any recognizable items except bird remains, and these could hardly have consisted of much other than duck prey. Duck prey was what littered the holes and the trails in the shore vegetation, the bodies of old birds and the young from two weeks to six weeks of age; victims everywhere, partly eaten or left intact except for the death wounds. The mother mink surely had splendid hunting, and, considering the way that those duckling broods were packed along the shore, it would have been surprising if she had not taken advantage of their availability.

The second most extreme case of my experience involved young coots at Mud Lake, north of Ruthven, Iowa, in 1933. Here the local minks ate little except coots for about a month, and the heaped droppings of latrines and the strewed remains about dens and trails revealed the carnage that was going on. But, with concentrations of coot nests approaching fifteen to twenty per acre in shore zone tracts of the marsh where the minks were accustomed to hunt, again it is not surprising that the minks were taking advantage of their opportunities while they had them. Even so, considering the tremendous number of coots reared at Mud Lake that summer, it may be doubted that the mink predation depressed the net productivity of the coot population very much.

At other times and places, I have seen almost whole latrines made up of yolk and shell fragments of coot and rail eggs when minks had access to large numbers of nests. The red down feathers and red bills and egg teeth of coots in the droppings often had enough shell fragments associated with them to indicate that the victims had been eaten while still in the eggs. It may not be possible to distinguish in many cases between newly hatched bird victims, those trying to get out of the eggs, and advanced embryos, but, in analyses of predation, this may not make much difference. The opportunism of the minks in combination with their opportunities can explain a great deal.

Among the unanswered questions that I see in mink-waterfowl relationships are those relating to predation upon what may be called the more normal densities of the birds living normal lives. It is clear that an occasional female may be killed on a nest, and that at least a minor nesting and rearing season toll may be taken by minks wherever waterfowl and minks occur together. A partly-eaten blue-winged teal hen with an egg in her oviduct, a pair of wings outside (or inside) a hole, littered bird debris under an overturned boat, a bird with small, paired, bloody punctures in head and neck lying beside a nest, downy birds or fledglings being worked over by carrion beetles, bluebottle flies going in and out of the caved-in tunnel of an old muskrat burrow, ducklings missing from a brood, the feathers and shells in droppings, miscellaneous evidence of predation here and there—all this is to be expected as part of the marshy scene within the breeding range of most North American waterfowl. It has been a part of the North American waterfowl equation for a long time, and there is plenty of evidence that minks and waterfowl are not completely lacking in adjustments to each other in places where both are native.

The reported intensity of mink predation upon Icelandic bird life seems excessive beyond anything ordinarily to be seen in the mink's native North American range.

The question may properly be asked if such intensity may not have some connection with the fact that the mink is an introduced species in Iceland. Racially, the Icelandic birds may not know what minks are, at any rate on their breeding grounds, and it is conceivable that some species may not be able to learn as rapidly as they may need to.

Appraisal of mink predation upon Icelandic waterfowl is not simplified by the high densities that many species of ducks attain on favored nesting grounds. Lake Myvatn, with an area of about thirteen square miles, has a very irregular outline, is rich in pondweeds but without emergent vegetation except for relatively minor growths of a sedge. Both its diving and dabbling ducks nest on the surrounding land. The ornithologist, Finnur Gudmundsson of Iceland, told me that the scaup was the most common duck at Myvatn, with an estimated nesting population of about ten thousand pairs; the tufted duck was second most common, and scoter and goldeneye populations each numbered about one thousand pairs. Add to these miscellaneous other divers as well as the mallard, gadwall, teal, pintail, and widgeon among the dabbling ducks, and the total may be figured as thousands of nesting ducks for every square mile of lake. Naturally, such a concentration of land-nesting ducks would be appreciated—wherever found—by the minks that could reach it.

The case history of the tree duck in Jamaica after introduction of the mongoose may afford insight into the sort of thing that logically could happen when wild minks become established in racially new range. According to J. C. Phillips,[32] the mongoose at first nearly exterminated the ground-nesting black-bellied tree duck. Then, a few of these ducks developed the safer habit of nesting in trees. Thereafter, with the adoption of this more advantageous way of life, the population of black-bellied tree ducks began gradually to recover.

Of course, it does not follow that Icelandic ducks have many alternatives that could assure their salvation from their new enemy. They might develop greater wariness, disperse their nest sites more, find nest sites less accessible to minks, or show more pronounced compensa-

tory trends in their population dynamics as time goes on.
Maybe they do not have any good answers.

SOME OF THE DEFICIENCIES in our understanding of
predation upon waterfowl are due, in part, to difficulties
in obtaining accurate information of the types needed.
Others are due, in part, to the psychological peculiarities
of many species of waterfowl which permit extremes of
both social tolerance and intolerance. The preferences
that migratory waterfowl show for congregating in one
place one year but not necessarily the next (or to a similar
extent) greatly complicate efforts to assess the real population effects of predation.

Despite their many inconclusive aspects, the existing
data suggest that compensatory adjustments may significantly modify the effect of predation in the population
dynamics of waterfowl, perhaps not quite to the extent
recorded for the quail, the pheasants, and the grouse, but
still enough to merit consideration.

The trumpeter swan is a species for which nearly
exact, long-term census figures have been obtained by
government personnel for its occupied range in the United
States—chiefly localized in northwestern Wyoming and
south-central Montana. Winston E. Banko[33] traced the
growth of this population from probably fewer than one
hundred in the early thirties to around seven hundred by
the late fifties and early sixties.

On the areas of the trumpeter swan range of this
region, predators known to prey upon the swans at some
stage of their life cycle were both abundant and scarce;
artificial repression of predators was practiced on some
areas and not on others, and some movements of swans
from one area to another were noted. But the trumpeter
swan populations showed patterns of growth similar to
those of the quail: as the overall population increased,
rates of gain decreased in ways that must reflect a very
considerable automatic adjustment in reproductive rates
and survival of young, whether losses took place through
predation or other agencies.

For the more common kinds of waterfowl, the evidence as to compensations and conformity to patterns is fragmentary yet suggestive, so far as it goes. Frank C. Bellrose and Elizabeth Brown Chase[34] compared the losses suffered by the mallard, the black duck, and the blue-winged teal and found some contrasts that would seem to indicate substitutions of mortality factors again reminiscent of what occurs in the population dynamics of the bobwhite. Of the above duck species, the mallard, which is the most heavily hunted by man, suffered the lowest "natural" losses; the blue-winged teal, the least hunted by man, suffered the highest "natural" losses; and the black duck, subject to intermediate intensities of human hunting, suffered "natural" losses intermediate between those of the mallard and teal. The authors felt that the shooting toll probably absorbed a large proportion of the mallard losses that otherwise would have occurred in an unshot population, and that the bluewings might be able to withstand considerably more human hunting without significantly raising their total mortality rates.

Other waterfowl data hint in much the same direction as the above, but I feel that that is as much as we are entitled to say on the basis of our present information. Lacking data of the more informative types concerning tendencies of waterfowl populations to reach and maintain certain levels and to compensate for losses from predation, we might appropriately think about what would be required to go significantly further in the study of these relationships. What kind of investigational groundwork would have to be laid before we could appraise, for example, the population impacts of predation upon wild ducks during the breeding months?

From the preliminary thinking I have done, I should say that, first of all, a suitable study area or combination of areas must have both resident predators and nesting ducks in sufficient numbers to obtain satisfactory data. The areas must be those in which it would be possible to keep fairly close track of both predator and duck populations and what they did—the study could not be carried on in just any place having the predators and the ducks. Not only must it be an area where the paths, dens, nests, pellets, droppings, and prey leavings of the predators could be found without excessive difficulty but also one permitting satisfactory counts of breeding ducks and their broods before local duck populations become mixed with newcomers in the course of late-summer adjustments and the beginning of the fall migration.

To insure the results that I would regard as meaningful, the wetland units chosen for regular observation should consist of a marsh or slough, or a combination of marshes and sloughs, lying sufficiently well isolated from other wetlands so that broods of ducklings would not be apt to make undetected journeys in or out of the study area. This would be a most important consideration. The nearest attractive wetlands should, in fact, be several miles away to discourage mother ducks from leading flightless broods overland in confusing movements. The places I know that would seem to offer the best possibilities for an accurate study of breeding populations and productivity of wild ducks are in the Nebraska Sand Hills and in the "pothole country" of western Minnesota, the eastern Dakotas, and the southern Prairie Provinces of Canada.

We might get informative results from such investigations if we did no more than measure the amount of predation exerted over a period of years by any predator or combination of predators upon accurately determined duck populations on a given study area. If we had fair luck as to weather and public cooperation and were able to find specimen material and to make brood counts, we might have at the end a defensible basis for judging population effects of predation upon the local ducks. This might be true for differing year-to-year population levels of predators and ducks, differing weather conditions, and differing practices in human land use. Maybe, we would have enough to draw clear conclusions, as the data would then stand.

Nevertheless, I think it would be safer also to obtain data on the population levels and fortunes of local wildlife other than the predators and the ducks. But, one might overreach in attempting to obtain data on the entire biotic communities represented by the wetlands and their surroundings. Despite what might be ideally desirable, an investigation having the scope I have in mind would just about have to be restricted by practical limitations.

What factors, in addition to the predators and the ducks, could feasibly be studied? Perhaps, from the standpoint of alternative prey of the predators, the investigation should include the breeding populations of coots and grebes, perhaps rails, terns, and blackbirds. Perhaps, some measurements or careful estimates should be made of populations of muskrats, of small rodents of the drier vegetation, even of crayfishes, grasshoppers, or other invertebrates that are important as predator foods. Perhaps, the biological consequences of one species of bird laying eggs in the nests of other species or engaging in other forms of "parasitism" should be studied.

Then, when year-to-year figures are down on paper—tabulated, worked and reworked, statistically refined, plotted against each other on coordinate paper, spread out to ponder over—some results may turn as expected and some might be a surprise. We might find competition within a species—as between pintails and pintails, between mallards and mallards—having a profound bearing upon the amount and the significance of the predation suffered. Or, the competition might be between species of ducks, possibly between ducks as a group—between mallards and pintails and ruddies and redheads. Maybe the coots and grebes would have competitive positions in these natural biological equations involving the ducks. Perhaps no competition for such obvious essentials of life as food would be apparent between waterfowl species having differing food habits; maybe the big question to be explored, if possible, in population analyses would be how much the mere presence of the different species affected the population status of another.

Maybe the species making up a waterfowl society would fit together perfectly, one complementing—not competing with—the other. It might well be expected that more manifestations of competition could result from relationships involving introduced species from other parts

of the world than from relationships already existing
among the North American ducks, grebes, coots, and some
other water birds that have been living together and
adjusting to each other for millions of years.

Of course, no one should predict results of any investigation of complex phenomena in advance of work accomplished. When marshes teem with birds of different kinds
yet having not wholly dissimilar habits or living requirements, and predators exploit the bird life according to
their opportunities, it may be very hard to say just how
the predation that one species suffers could be affected by
the presence of other prey species. It may be very hard to
say just what constitutes opportunities for predation and
just how the various interlinked populations maintain
themselves as they do.

One possibility that should not be neglected is that
some species might serve as "buffers," thus diverting some
of the predation that other species might suffer. This concept is often treated in the literature, sometimes with fair
evidence in its favor, sometimes with the visible evidence
seeming to point in the opposite direction.

Another possibility is that the conspicuous presence
of one species may sometimes work to the disadvantage of
others by attracting predators to a place. In my own experience, I have felt that the presence of wintering mallards increased the uneasiness if not the actual vulnerability of bobwhites feeding at the same station, though there
were no overt displays of antagonism between the two
species. On a marshy pothole, differential mortality or
other disadvantages could select against the less resilient
or the less well situated species as inexorably as could
active competition between species; and the many different species of waterfowl on the potholes may not all be
assured of equal success in taking care of themselves if
their collective abundance draws the attention of formidable and persistent predators.

9

PREDATION AND THE MUSKRAT: WHEN THE PATTERNS STILL LOOKED FAIRLY SIMPLE

As a South Dakota fur trapper in my teens and twenties, I learned something about what muskrats were and something about the way they lived. In taking hundreds of the animals for fur, I developed a certain skill in trapping and, also, in "shucking" off their skins and fastening them onto the stretching boards. But like most other trappers, I overestimated what I really learned about muskrats from trapping experiences and casual observations, and shall not dignify anything I then did by calling it research.

It was not until after joining the Iowa State College faculty in 1932 that I actually began scientific studies of the muskrat and these began, in a way, with studies of predator food habits. Of 409 horned owl pellets gathered from five stream and oxbow territories, fall through summer, 1932–33, ten contained muskrat remains; and of these ten, nine were from one lot of thirty-one pellets. All but one of the muskrats represented in the nine pellets were young animals and the field evidence indicated that the victims had been occupants of small, shallow, and food-poor oxbows in a wooded pasture. This all made sense.

The next year I examined some pellets from a horned owl territory on an island in a three hundred-acre tract of marsh called Mud Lake, north of Ruthven in northwest Iowa. It might have been expected that a predator reputed

147

to be such a fearsome muskrat enemy as the horned owl would take advantage of muskrats crowded into a marsh. Yet no muskrat remains were found in eighty-nine pellets that I examined from the island, from spring through fall of 1933, although the tract of marsh had at the time a population of between fifteen hundred and two thousand muskrats. Nearly three hundred pellets from four other horned owl territories included eight with muskrat remains. Six of the muskrat-containing pellets were in one lot of thirty-two—all from areas having far fewer muskrats than the Mud Lake area. These other areas were patently less suited to accommodate large numbers of muskrats than was the marsh with the island.

So far, the predation of horned owls upon muskrats reminded me of the predation of horned owls upon quail at Prairie du Sac. Nevertheless, some aspects of the predation involving muskrats did not look at all clear. Mink dens about northwest Iowa marshes might be littered with muskrat remains and some lots of mink droppings might consist entirely of muskrat bones and fur.

During the summer of 1934 I made a start on a serious study of Iowa muskrats. Scientifically, my work was simplified by a drought severe enough to mean emergency conditions for the muskrats of a large part of the state. The drought emergency virtually guaranteed interesting and tangible results from the muskrat study, even if one made allowance for trial and error and the necessity for developing techniques. The emergency could be followed in at least a fairly satisfactory manner without any particular planning except for an observer to be and stay on the scene while things were happening naturally.

It was true that the intensity and biological impacts of the 1934 drought varied locally and that it did not make muskrats perceptibly more vulnerable to horned owl predation in those parts of central or northwestern Iowa where pellet collections were obtained. Only one of nearly two hundred pellets dated to the drought period contained muskrat remains, and that victim was a young animal. However, the finding of thirty-eight muskrats among 2,848 prey items examined from Iowa red fox dens in 1934, compared with only two muskrats in 1,010 items in 1933, seemed linked with greater vulnerability of the muskrats during the dry spring of 1934. The observations I made on mink predation upon muskrats were interesting enough to me, but I could not be sure whether they did or did not reflect drought conditions.

As the summer went on, I began to realize I was not learning as much as I wanted to about muskrats through the drought emergency after all. Of course, I learned some things through observation and taking field notes on what I thought was significant; but, after investing the greater part of the summer in general observations on drying streams in central Iowa and on two northwestern marshes, I could see I needed to make the field studies more systematic.

THE MUSKRAT WORK for 1935 was centered during the spring and summer on two marshes in northwest Iowa, both north of Ruthven. Of the two marshes, the state-owned 450-acre Round Lake was set up as a major study area for at least a five-year period. The procedure here was to map the location of all muskrat habitations, mark young muskrats with numbered metal tags to facilitate studies of growth rates and movements, and then record as much as possible the happenings during the breeding season. Some adult females could be individually recognized from their appearance or habits. Territories of others were sufficiently isolated so that they were known to be maintained by certain individuals. Special attention was paid to mortality of muskrats of all ages and to food habits and hunting methods of the minks that frequented the marsh edge.

The magnitude of the juvenile mortality suffered by the observed muskrat populations that year was startling— most of it due to attacks by older muskrats. In some places, the slaughter of the innocents was so great as to almost nullify reproductive efforts throughout the breeding months. Life among the muskrats proved to be a most hectic succession of fights, evictions, trespasses, abandonment of litters, and other troubles. Young animals died of a skin disease caused by one of the "ringworm" fungi known to mycologists as *Trichophyton mentagrophytes.* They were preyed upon by minks. They were eaten by cannibalistic members of their own kind. About the only places where weaned young could regularly be seen were on rush rafts in company with tolerant adults. At this time, I thought that the muskrat as a species required a high reproductive rate to exist at all in view of its excessive reproductive wastage.

As research results, the 1935 data from especially Round Lake were of good quality and highly informative. But I mistakenly assumed that what I saw typified the breeding fortunes of muskrat populations, when in fact what I then observed was far from typical. I did not, as yet, have sufficient perspective to recognize that my first intensive work had been done with a biologically top-heavy population afflicted with most of the ills to which muskrat flesh is subject.

What I saw were genuine happenings. It was true that a mother muskrat might bite to death another mother's litter of young and then take over the nest for her own young. It was true that four of five newly weaned young might be bitten to death by other muskrats, including their own parents. Mink families did subsist for weeks largely upon young muskrats. Death and the "sign" of death could become a most conspicuous feature of a muskrat marsh.

Five female minks with their litters of young were localized in the shore zone bordering about half of Round Lake. From a quarter to a half of the summer's mink droppings contained remains of young muskrats. In early summer, the young muskrats seemed to be preyed upon so heavily chiefly because there were so many of them. In late summer, the young muskrats infected with the fungus skin disease suffered disproportionately heavier mink predation than did healthy young of similar ages kept under comparable conditions.

It would seem reasonable that parent muskrats not displaying very strong solicitude toward healthy litters would be unlikely to care well for patently unthrifty ones. The sufferers from the fungus disease, with their corrugated skin folds and hairless patches and stunted growth, did not look to me like anything their mothers would especially wish to have around. I do not consider it unrealistic to give a muskrat mother credit for knowing something about what a young muskrat *should* be.

Possibly, there were other reasons why diseased young were more vulnerable to minks than were healthy young. Listening outside of lodges containing diseased litters, I frequently heard the young whimpering in their misery, and minks passing nearby doubtless could have heard the whimpering too.

From the population standpoint, it seemed to make no difference in the end whether minks did or did not kill the diseased young muskrats. The course of the disease was so uniformly deadly among unweaned litters that the appearance of disease lesions on the body of one member usually meant the loss of the entire litter.

Nor did other evidence signify much real population effect of the mink predation upon the young muskrats. The parts of the marsh on which the mink predation was most severe reared, tract for tract, about the same number of muskrats during the breeding months as did the parts that were mink-free. On the mink-free parts, the muskrats not only were their own chief agency of mortality, but their breeding efforts also virtually ceased by midsummer. On the parts having the heavy mink predation there was decidedly less actual killing of muskrat by muskrat and breeding occurred as late in the summer as August. The 1935 case history of the Round Lake muskrat population revealed a great deal of natural substitution of different types of mortality and compensatory adjustment.

The second marsh on which intensive studies were carried on in 1935 was the same Mud Lake that had the horned owl territory on the island in 1933.

At Mud Lake, the most conspicuous single event in 1935 was the collapse from natural though undetermined cause of about a third of the bulrush stand of the marsh. Prior to the collapse a breeding population of nearly one thousand adult muskrats, together with an estimated population of between three thousand and thirty-five hundred young, had lived with evident security from horned owls again nesting on the island. A single pellet from late May—in a collection of 148 deposited mostly in March, April, and May—contained remains of a young muskrat; then, at the time of collapse of the bulrushes, five of sixteen June pellets and eight of twelve July pellets contained muskrat remains. Remains of one adult and eleven young muskrats were distinguished in the eight muskrat-containing pellets for July.

For many hundreds of muskrats, adults and young, their habitat was there; then it was gone. And when it was gone, the muskrats remained for a time trying their best to survive. The time was opportune for predators. That much I could see on the spot, even though I lacked data and experience from which to interpret the evidence more fully.

On the central Iowa stream areas, I noted in a tentative way in 1935 such retreats as seemed to be territorial centers of the muskrats and, for these, I began a long-term series of records. In this year I also began regular visits to another central Iowa area—state-owned Little Wall Lake, a marsh of 270 acres.

By 1936, I HAD ESTABLISHED some more areas for regular observation of muskrats, in both central and northwestern Iowa. The excessively hot, dry summer really brought trouble to muskrat populations. As the water disappeared from their habitats, luckless animals fought among themselves, abandoned familiar ranges to wander, died of heat and thirst, and were killed by minks.

Nevertheless, what were in many ways the most informative data of 1936 came from Round Lake, which retained sufficient water for most of its muskrats even at the worst of the drought. Exposure of the shore zone was accompanied by wholly expected mink predation upon the exposed parts of the muskrat population, but much of interest happened that had no possible connection with the drought.

In April and May, Round Lake's rather low population of approximately two hundred adult muskrats lost about twenty of their number (eighteen victims were examined), chiefly through mink predation. The brunt of this predation was borne by socially unassimilated, fight-battered males that congregated along shore, living in temporary nests directly in lines of travel of the local minks.

Sixty-one of 106 mink droppings examined from Round Lake for this period of muskrat vulnerability contained muskrat remains. By the middle of June, the battered shore dwellers had been eliminated, the incidence of muskrat remains was down to seven in eighty-four mink droppings, and the rest of the muskrats were living with security from their usual predatory enemies.

The midsummer muskrat population was not, however, exempt from its own vicious frictions, its own deadly behavior patterns, and from losses occurring through disease. Again, in 1936 as in 1935, I had insufficient background for appraising some of the major happenings that I was seeing but the field data put down on paper ultimately had more meaning.

My techniques for intensive field work at Round Lake were considerably improved in 1936 over what they had been in 1935, and the resulting data may still be classed as among the most comprehensive and accurate obtained from any of our Iowa muskrat areas. I made a special effort to handle and trace the fortunes of every litter of muskrats born on the marsh throughout the breeding season. This meant examination of the lodges—using great care not to unduly disturb the helpless young kept therein—about every week or two in rotation for three months. While the results fell short of the full objectives aimed at, they did provide some singular details on life history and population phenomena.

Continued marking studies reinforced the overall study program in several ways. They proved the identity of weaned young found bitten to death in the lodges just before their mother gave birth to her next litter. They proved the identity of litters kept divided, each of two parts in separate nests, sometimes in separate lodges lying up to sixty yards apart. They proved rules and exceptions to rules in certain cases.

Through marking, the essentially sedentary behavior of the marsh-dwelling muskrat population was demonstrated. All but two of twelve tagged animals taken on the marsh for specimens in the fall and winter of 1936–37 were taken within three hundred yards of their birthplaces. At another extreme was an animal killed early in that same winter in a farmer's hog house about twenty-one miles away from where it had been tagged at its Round Lake birthplace in 1935. Another tagged animal demonstrated that recovery from the fungus skin disease, while infrequent, was still possible.

The breeding season fortunes of the Round Lake muskrats were further studied through examination of 175 specimens taken on the marsh in November and December. In addition to the special value of the twelve marked animals among the specimens, the sex and age ratios shown by a good sample of the local population enabled me to piece together the rest of the 1936 story of events at Round Lake. The data from the fall and early winter specimens constituted, in short, the pay-off for the months of careful work during the spring and summer. When properly used in connection with information already in possession, the specimen ratios provided a basis for calculating both the fall population level of the muskrats and the net reproductive efficiency of the population during the breeding season.

From a settled breeding population the equivalent of eighty pairs, or a total of about 170 adults, the population rose to a calculated 422 by fall, a rate of gain of 147 per cent. The number of litters born per female ranged from none to four, averaging a little less than two. Years later I could see that the fall population and the season's reproduction were both lower than could have been accounted for in ordinary terms of drought exposure, population pressure, disease losses, or predation. Could there be any connection between what happened to the Round Lake muskrats in 1936 and the peculiarly depressed rate of gain of the Prairie du Sac quail—and the "low cycle" stages of Lake States' grouse and hares? Here was something to think about when the time came.

At Mud Lake, the 1936 spring population was something over the equivalent of 160 pairs, or probably about 350 adults. In the fall, 501 muskrats were taken in nearly annihilative trapping. Forty-two of these were the population remnants occupying a drought-exposed area of about one hundred acres; but, as at Round Lake, it would seem to require more than the drought to explain the poor spring to fall recovery of Mud Lake's muskrats.

Some wandering muskrats did congregate about the edge and work over the ice of Round Lake and Mud Lake in late fall and winter and these usually could be recognized at a glance. They were young and they were old; they were of either sex; but they were characteristically thin and chewed up from encounters with other muskrats. They sat in nests improvised in shore zone vegetation, their kidneys exposed by bites, gashes across sides and rumps, tails bitten through, bites on faces and forelegs as well as hindquarters, fight wounds in all stages of healing. They hobbled across open spaces or through rushes and weeds, bleeding, trying to find food and shelter and to keep out of trouble. They were dying from hunger or cold, their tails, feet, and eyes freezing—or dying from their fight wounds, or being killed by mink or fox or dog or bird of prey. The bodies of the dead would be eaten upon by minks, foxes, crows, or by other muskrats. Or, out on the ice, the frozen body of a wanderer might lie uneaten by anything, but it would reek of fox urine and have a fox dropping left on top of it to mark a claim. Or the dead body might show the special insult of droppings from some other wandering muskrat heaped upon it.

Whatever else might be said of these wandering muskrats, they usually represented wastage, and, from the standpoint of the population biology of the species, it did not matter much what befell them. They were targets for anything predatory that came along and could handle them.

MORE MARKING OF YOUNG muskrats was done in connection
with intensive studies at Round Lake in 1938, and 204
specimens of resident animals were examined during late
November and early December. Data from the trapped
sample, used in combination with breeding-season
censuses, gave a fall population of 750, or a rate of gain of
over 400 per cent from the spring population.

Although the mink population at Round Lake was
low during the summer of 1938 (a single litter of young
minks and their mother), mink predation upon muskrats
was fairly substantial. Thirteen of 399 summer mink
droppings contained remains of young muskrats. It could
be seen that most victims were of recently weaned litters
kept near the marsh edge, and that they were killed while
engaging in such dangerous activities ashore as frequenting the attractive land trails worn through thick vegetation
by the minks themselves.

The central Iowa muskrat studies of 1938 were of
routine nature, yielding data that were valuable when
considered along with data from other years. All that need
be further mentioned of these studies here is that they
initiated a standard technique henceforth followed on all
muskrat areas that I kept under regular observation. First,
in May or June I recorded the location of centers of activity characteristic of maintained territories. Then during
summer and fall I sought all other field data that might
be needed or useful. Finally, I examined population
samples trapped by the public for fur in late fall or early
winter from or near my observational areas. The fur-
trapping season usually opened on November 10, or at a
time when muskrat specimens were in ideal condition for
post-mortem examination.

In practice—although I did not know it at the time—
the fall population status of an area's muskrats might be
calculated as simply as by applying the sex and age ratios
of the trapped samples to the numbers of breeding territories present in the spring. Sometimes the warm weather
fortunes of the muskrats would be so uneventful that no
corrections had to be made for losses of adult females, for
movements of animals into or out of the study areas, or

for much of anything else in pro rata calculations. At other times, the local situations might become so thoroughly complicated by movements, drought emergencies, epidemics, or by other upsetting factors, that pro rata calculations using fall sex and age ratios and spring censuses would be misleading if used without proper corrections. And at times, about the only way to obtain fall population figures would be to examine essentially entire population groups as trapped specimens. I was able to do that in a number of cases, with the help given me by particularly cooperative trappers.

IN 1939 OTHER AREAS were put under regular observation. I started work on three state-owned marshes: Cheever Lake (380 acres) and Four-Mile Lake (219 acres), lying west of Estherville in northwestern Iowa, and Wall Lake (935 acres), in north-central Iowa. More central Iowa streams were added to the study areas, mainly so that data could be obtained from a greater diversity of muskrat habitats—from brooks, tile flows, ditches, all the way up to medium-sized streams. At their maximum the Iowa study areas included, in a total of nearly forty square miles, the places where muskrats lived or could be expected to try to live.

In the fall of 1939 a long dry Indian summer left the muskrats so greatly reduced over most of Iowa that the Conservation Commission gave them protection from trapping during the legal fur season. This meant that I would have no fall-trapped specimens from the cooperating public, but the drought crisis became so bad that I felt I could make fair estimates of the population remnants on most of my study areas from "sign." My experience as a muskrat trapper in South Dakota gave me some basis for doing this. I would walk along, examine the deepened burrow systems and the mud-plastered lodges and the bubbles and food particles under the ice, and think back to my trapping years. I would then estimate the number of muskrats I could have expected to catch from a place showing similar "sign," and put the figure down in my notes as my best estimate. Such estimates would still be only estimates, but, when carefully made, I think that they came close to the actual number of animals present.

The Conservation Commission obtained from state-owned Round Lake and Cheever Lake the series of fall-trapped specimens needed to complete the breeding season and post-breeding studies of muskrats conducted on these marshes. That gave me some fall specimen material I could count on, though from places subject to only moderately severe drought exposure. Both marshes, however, had interesting predator situations.

Apparently, only a solitary big mink was regularly present at Round Lake during the spring and summer of 1939. Three of nineteen spring droppings contained muskrat remains, and the two mink victims that I then examined were representative of the several homeless muskrats that were living in flimsy nests along shore. The one live wanderer collected for examination in April had painful looking strife wounds. Muskrat remains were found in four of 150 mink droppings deposited in June and July and in none of ninety-two for September.

In this case, the mink predation was centered more upon adult muskrats than upon the young. Of an early May population, the equivalent of two hundred pairs (about 425 adults), about 107 pairs lived in shore-zone territories that became drought exposed in late summer and early fall. In these, the adult females tended to hang on to their "old homesteads" until it was too late for them to make safe adjustments. As drought conditions became worse with the approach of freeze-up, so did the status of the adults of the shore zones. The shore zones were also the places where desperate wanderers from the general countryside tended to congregate, adding to the troubles of the residents.

In contrast, most of the shore-zone young took care of themselves better than their elders under the circumstances. After the breeding season was over and during a time when strange muskrats could move among established residents with the best chance of being socially accepted, most of the shore-zone young moved out into the deeper parts of the marsh and established themselves there as reasonably secure residents. They were therefore largely still alive by early winter and showed up prominently in a state-trapped sample of 195 residents. In this sample there were 165 young of the year, sixteen adult males, and fourteen adult females.

It was notable that, despite the scarcity of predators, by the time of the trapping the parent muskrats of the shore zone were largely dead from predation or fighting or from weather emergencies, or were wandering and dying from natural causes. Because of this excessive loss of shore-zone adults, the total population could not be calculated by direct application of the sex and age ratios of the trapped sample to the number of breeding season territories. After the proper allowances were made, the grand total of resident muskrats remaining at Round Lake, as of the late fall and early winter of 1939–40, appeared to be approximately 1,280.

Cheever Lake and its associated sloughs in 1939 afforded an opportunity to study a far more complex situation than did Round Lake. Accordingly, the Cheever Lake area was made the site of intensive work throughout most of the summer and fall and on into the winter, until the winter work was terminated with the trapping by the Conservation Commission of ninety-seven specimens from representative wet and dry parts. As at Round Lake, and for the same technical reasons, the sex and age ratios from the specimens trapped from Cheever Lake could not be applied directly to the number of breeding-season territories, but the very detailed field data from Cheever Lake permitted calculations on a tract-by-tract basis.

The Cheever Lake wetlands had an initial breeding population that was the equivalent of 332 pairs, or about 780 adults. By early winter, after a summer and fall of increasing drought crisis, the total muskrat population was about 1,765, of which all but eighty-five were concentrated on the less than 150 acres still having surface water. The mink population that was present to take advantage of the drought vulnerability of the muskrats consisted of a

mother with her family of young, plus possibly two adult
males during spring and summer.

On the whole, the occupants of the deep-water tracts
of marsh got along well, as did the young that moved into
the deeper tracts from drying shore zones in late summer.
The post-breeding adjustments here were exactly of the
sorts described for Round Lake, and the adults that retained their dried out shore-zone territories until late fall
were subject to the same sorts of deadly troubles. It was
in the shallow marshes and sloughs extending away from
the main body of water at Cheever Lake that the adjustments had their most dramatic aspects.

Original territorial holdings in the shallows were
sometimes retained and sometimes abandoned by the
muskrats during the weeks and months of drought exposure. In three well-studied cases, groups of tenaciously held
territories in such strategic places as the necks of narrow
marshes blocked the movements of conspicuous numbers
of muskrats that tried to make adjustments in the direction
of the remaining wet marsh. Such occupied groups of
territories functioned as biological dams, holding back for
a time the restless homeless animals collecting on one side.
The way it looked to me, it may have been the dominant
concentrated scent of the animals resident in the blocking
territories that served to deter the invasion from the dry
sloughs.

Finally, the "dams" broke and the adjusting masses
flowed through, spreading along the shore zones of the
main wet area, complicating life for the territory holders
still trying to live there. One place the homeless newcomers practically overwhelmed with their numbers was
a five-acre tract lying in and next to the natural outlet (the
main avenue of travel) of the wet marsh. On the evening
of September 27, around thirty muskrats per acre were in
sight at once on the five acres and the majority of these
were new invaders. Following this massing there was also
a brief countermovement back through the outlet into the
dry marsh—which still had more attractive food resources
than the invaded wet part. In addition, many muskrats
abandoned the whole Cheever Lake area, heading cross-
country as wanderers.

The unhappy status of the wanderers is illustrated by specimens shot for examination between late September and the middle of November. Of seven specimens, only two (both young animals) were without strife wounds, and the five adults in the sample all had severe strife wounds. During the same period many dead animals were found, of which ten were in sufficiently fresh condition to show that they had died of strife wounds; and of these ten, all but one were adults.

All of this unrest, friction, and drought exposure could be expected to draw predation, and it did. Muskrat remains in eighty-one of 212 mink droppings deposited from July to the middle of November reflected the acute vulnerability of especially the young muskrats in the dry shallows. As winter came on, the chronic wanderers of the shore zones were the chief victims of what few minks were present, but this had no apparent population significance to the muskrats. Most of the ill-situated muskrats at or in the vicinity of Cheever Lake were dead by midwinter, 1939–40, whether subject to mink predation or not. Nor did it seem to make much difference to the muskrats what other predators were present, including horned owls and red foxes. Twenty-two specimens were collected from the muskrats still living in the shore zones and shallows by early January, and these illustrated the social difficulties that the animals were having. Six of the twenty-two specimens had recent wounds from fighting among themselves, and five of the others had older wound scars. Ten of the twenty-two were adults, and these adults had most of the strife wounds. There was also some evidence of muskrats feeding on muskrat bodies from fall to midwinter, though I do not know how much of this may have represented killing of muskrats by muskrats.

Wall Lake, in north-central Iowa, was the scene of great contrasts in vulnerability and security during the fall and winter of 1939–40. It had a total of thirty-four acres remaining wet enough to have muskrats in residence by fall, and the total muskrat population was calculated at about 280. Minks were conspicuously abundant. An estimated six to eight hunted the thirty-four acres of muskrat-occupied marsh. One tract of fifteen acres remained in good condition for the muskrats and wintered about 190 of the 210 trying to live there, despite assiduous digging into lodges by minks. Elsewhere, in the shallower tracts, an estimated eighteen to twenty of an original seventy muskrats survived the winter, but these muskrats suffered more mortality through fighting among themselves, through the stringencies of wintering, and through the attacks by a farm dog than they did through mink predation.

The next year Wall Lake became drought-exposed in midsummer after a favorable spring and early summer for the muskrats living in those tracts (totaling thirty-four acres, as in 1939) that were habitable for muskrats. The breeding-season population of about one hundred adults, plus between five hundred and seven hundred young, had been living securely despite the presence of the heavy local population of several adult minks and one litter of young minks.

By June 20, about half of the thirty-four-acre area occupied by the muskrats was exposed, except for puddles, and a family of red foxes had begun to show interest in the thirty to fifty muskrats that were traveling back and forth over the mud between their lodges and favored feeding grounds. By early August, the receding water had exposed the feeding grounds of a total of about 250 muskrats, the latter having a ratio of about one adult per two young. Eleven of thirty-five mink droppings contained muskrat remains, but the minks did not do too well in competition with the foxes for the vulnerable members of the muskrat population. Sixty-nine of seventy-three fox droppings datable to this period of drought exposure contained muskrat remains, and the field "sign" revealed a specialized type of predation. The adult foxes stationed themselves beside trails and picked up the young muskrats that tried to run past when the young foxes ranged about.

Mid-August rains relieved the drought crisis for a surviving muskrat population of something over two hundred, though the marsh bottom became completely exposed again in September. The foxes did not take advantage of the muskrats during the second drought exposure, however, and only three of 162 fox droppings examined from late August, 1940, to early March, 1941, contained muskrat remains. Muskrat remains were found in thirteen of fifty-nine mink droppings for late summer and fall, which reflected continued exploitation of muskrats after the foxes lost interest in the muskrat-occupied part of the marsh and hunted elsewhere.

The Wall Lake studies of predation in 1940 introduced something new in my experience with predator-prey relationships, and I had the further advantage of working in close cooperation with Thomas G. Scott,[35] who was studying the behavior and food habits of red foxes. Between us, we felt that we had figured out the sequences in the local predation drama quite well.

Those enterprising and "foxy" foxes seemed able to prey upon especially the drought-handicapped young muskrats weeks ahead of any ordinary schedule of mortality through mink predation. At the same time, adult muskrats could take care of themselves. After making allowance for what the muskrat mortality would likely have been in the absence of the foxes, I estimated that the uncompensated net loss caused by these foxes amounted to as many as one hundred muskrats. In other words, had it not been for the specialized attentions of the foxes there might have been up to three hundred muskrats present by late fall instead of the two hundred that were there.

CENTRAL IOWA STREAMS AND ponds provided some instructive case histories in 1942. Two small, adjacent ponds surrounded by cornfields had the equivalent of four breeding pairs of muskrats in the spring of 1942. Fifteen litters born to the four adult females were accounted for, these totaling about 125 young, and there were indications that another litter was born, thus giving an average of four litters per female. As of mid-August, the population was estimated at about fifty adult and nearly grown muskrats, plus about twenty young born in midsummer and later. By late fall, the population remaining was probably around sixty.

I do not know how much of the difference between

the number of young born and the number remaining by
late fall may have been due to emigration. I know that
there was substantial reproductive wastage, despite the
richness of the food supply. Late-season breeding occurred
on what might be called a full scale, but the survival of
late-born young was poor. Muskrats were killed by muskrats and during the low-water stages of late summer muskrats were killed by predators. Although no muskrat
remains were found in ninety-six mink droppings examined from the vicinity of the ponds in May, June, and
July, eleven of fifty-eight August droppings contained
remains representing members of at least five litters. Then,
after this biological "shaking down" of overproduced
young was over, no further evidence of mink predation
upon the muskrats was seen from September through the
rest of the fall.

A pasture brook fed by a county drain was the site of

considerable dog predation upon members of a family group of muskrats during August. The dog was large, powerful, and a diligent digger, and as it dug out one set of burrows the adult muskrats responded by making new burrows. Muskrats of active sizes avoided the dog by swimming from one burrow entrance to another, taking advantage of the concealment offered by submerged plant growths. The dog probably killed most of the members of two late-born (August and September?) litters, though the members of two litters born earlier in the summer were fairly successful in escaping. By late fall, about ten muskrats were still present in this out-of-the-way place.

Flood waters were very destructive to helpless sizes of young muskrats along many stretches of central Iowa streams in the late spring and early summer of 1942. The floods came at such times and with such severity as to drown almost all young born to local stream populations before the middle of June. Yet these losses seemed to have been biologically compensated, and the twenty square miles of central Iowa stream habitats kept under regular observation had, by fall, about as many muskrats as they could have been expected to accommodate, anyway. From the spring level of seventy-eight breeding territories (occupied by about 180 adults) on the twenty square miles, a fall population of about 750 represented one of the higher rates of gain in our records for the area.

The severe early losses of young from flooding were compensated not only by most of the adult females giving birth to three or four litters each (instead of their more usual two or three litters for the breeding season) but also by a higher survival rate of late-born young. Under ordinary conditions, late-born litters suffer disproportionate mortality as habitats fill up with muskrats. In 1942, early losses delayed the filling up of central Iowa streams with muskrats to the extent that late litters survived as well as early ones usually did. Nearly 20 per cent of the eighty-nine specimens of young of the year trapped in the fall of 1942 from central Iowa streams consisted of young born in August or later. This was about three times the usual proportion of late-born young to be found in the trappers' catches.

Although in the above instance the losses of young muskrats were due to an agency other than predation, they are pertinent to our discussion of predation. They help illustrate how the natural balancing and counterbalancing in populations may go on, how losses may be severe without being biologically overwhelming, how even severe losses may not necessarily count in really depressing a population. If we wish to, we could theoretically substitute predation for drowning losses in the equation, with some expectation of arriving at correct conclusions—except that predation is much less likely to cut severely into the early production of muskrats than are deadly floods.

IN THE SPRING of 1943, I had a technical bulletin in press—an analysis of mink predation upon muskrats.[36] While I knew that I had not written the last word on such a complex subject, I did feel that the years of professional field work plus early fur-trapping experience should have given me a reasonably good background for a thorough treatment. I had by then more or less experience with minks and muskrats over a period of twenty-eight years.

In the hope of avoiding the more tiresome delineations that the piles of field notes could lead into, I shall simply skip details and summarize the conclusions arrived at during the preparation of the bulletin on mink and muskrat relationships.

Six major generalizations as to mink predation upon muskrats had shaped up by the end of the first five years of the Iowa studies; and these continued to be valid not only through the time of preparation of the bulletin but also through the later years. They were:

One—Adult muskrats sufficiently well-situated as "property owners" to maintain regular home ranges or territories during the breeding months are practically safe from mink predation as long as their habitats remain in good condition. The converse is that those same muskrats can suffer severe mink predation when put at a great disadvantage, as through drought exposure.

Two—Adult muskrats that do not enjoy the social advantages of established residents during the breeding months may or may not be able to defend themselves against or escape from the more formidable minks they encounter. Muskrats that are still habitual transients by late spring tend to suffer injuries from attacks by territorial defenders and to withdraw into the poorer environmental habitats. As surplus individuals, they tend to congregate along the edges of lakes and marshes, directly in the lines of travel of many minks.

Three—Young muskrats born to well-situated populations ordinarily are not subject to much mink predation, even when many muskrat-hungry minks are about. Apart from emergencies due to drought exposures, floods, etc., the main factor making large numbers of young muskrats vulnerable to predation is overproduction of young by the breeding population. Minks prey upon such overproduced young, particularly when the latter are attacked by other muskrats and thus forced into hazardous ways of life, as when forced ashore from the more crowded wetter parts of marshes.

Four—Mink predation upon muskrats during the post-breeding months of late summer and fall tends to be negligible except in the event of complications from drought, storms, or muskrats invading places already occupied to capacity by other muskrats. This relative security follows naturally as a result of both the earlier shaking down of population surpluses and of the much easier social relationships prevailing among muskrats after the end of the breeding season and while the problems of approaching winter are still in the future. It can be a mellow time of year for comfortable muskrat populations and few comfortable muskrats need let themselves be killed by minks.

Five—Early winter mink predation upon muskrats, like that of late summer and fall, tends to be light and sporadic and centered upon homeless, restless, and drought-exposed individuals.

Six—From midwinter through early spring,

minks may prey heavily upon muskrats made vulnerable by either environmental or social stresses. Any sinking of frost lines that seals off the food supply of muskrats trying to live in shallows and makes them increasingly subject to starvation and freezing also makes them increasingly subject to mink predation. Late-winter mink predation is often centered upon such muskrats as become restless or are forced out of previously secure wintering quarters with the approach of the breeding season. The individuals that especially draw this predation often start coming out on the ice during thaws, sometimes many weeks in advance of the real spring dispersal. Also, severe predation upon them tends to be followed by absence of battered habitual transients in late spring. The latter social class of animals evidently consists of the same individuals that tend to behave in a restless or insecure manner long before any general schedule of spring movements.

Throughout all of the complex and varying case histories of muskrat populations in hand at the time of preparation of the bulletin manuscript, the fundamental role of the muskrat's intolerance of crowding stood out as a limiting factor. Like the intolerance underlying thresholds of security shown by the bobwhite quail, the intolerance of the muskrat could differ according to the locality, the year, the time of year, and the impacts of emergencies. Nevertheless, it was there and dominant to such an extent that even the most exceptional combinations of other variables seldom did more than partially obscure it.

Like the quail data, the muskrat data supported, in my opinion, the concept of populations conforming to mathematical patterns set by the behavior of the species in relation to the particular features of the environmental tracts occupied. The fact that those self-limiting patterns were thus conformed to seemed in itself proof of much resilience in rates of gain and loss—proof of much automatic substituting and compensating in especially the loss rates. When part of the population exceeded the secure level for a given area, that part amounted to little more than wastage, and the exact fate of wastage animals through this or that agency had its immaterial aspects in determining what really were limiting factors.

When mink predation upon muskrats was considered from this perspective, the severest observed losses seemed to have scant net effect on Iowa muskrat populations as long as those populations lived in environments suitable for them. Nearly all that minks ever were able to do as predators upon muskrats was to prey upon some of the more expendable parts of the muskrat populations.

The only data then in hand—as of the spring of 1943—that did not fit in with this picture were from certain local muskrat populations that seemed to have been well-situated for wintering yet still were vulnerable to mink predation. Later, it became clear that the otherwise inexplicable exploitation of these muskrats by minks represented scavenging upon victims of epidemic disease rather than predation, but that is reserved for discussion in the following chapter.

BY THE EARLY FORTIES, I also had my routine for the long-term Iowa field studies standardized as much as it ever would be. I had largely discontinued the field work on some of the less productive study areas (especially those too far away to visit at satisfactory intervals), and the central and north-central Iowa areas retained for year-after-year study comprised the muskrat habitats in twenty-seven square miles of land.

I did not know what I was going to learn from those twenty-seven square miles, from the spring of 1943 through the next fifteen years. I planned to continue estimating the number of breeding territories each year from mid-May to mid-June, following through with the field work to keep track of the significant happenings on each area throughout summer and fall—the impacts of droughts or floods or human engineering, the detectable mortality, or the movement trends in and out of the areas. There would be the usual gathering of statistics on numbers and dates of birth of litters born to local muskrat females, the marking of young muskrats living in strategic places, the mapping and the verifying of territories, the large-scale examination of mink and fox and raccoon droppings in places where the muskrats were having trouble, and the post-mortem examination of dead muskrats wherever found. There would be the trapped muskrat carcasses to examine, the placental scars to count and age and compare, if possible, with breeding data obtained earlier in the course of each season's field studies.

My principal aim in establishing a more stabilized procedure of study on definite land units was to get more accurate data of the types that might bring out more information about the rules of order in population dynamics of the muskrats.

I did not expect that such rules of order would necessarily ever be easy to figure out, even with years of statistics and charts and maps from which to figure.

10

MORE ABOUT PREDATION
AND THE MUSKRAT

I WAS NOT LOOKING FOR another study area in 1941 when I joined the gun club that leased shooting rights on privately owned Goose Lake, a marsh of about 135 acres in the same neighborhood as Little Wall Lake. I merely wanted a place where I could go duck hunting and relax in the out-of-doors, and this marsh about twenty-five miles from home seemed to be the place.

In fact, as I thoroughly covered Goose Lake during my first hunting season there, I regarded the muskrats chiefly as being an interesting part of the local surroundings. I gave them little special attention unless I happened to see something interesting, such as mink-killed animals in drought-exposed shallows or strife-battered transients trying to find a place to live—all worth noticing but still all quite to be expected under the circumstances and nothing to compete unduly with the hunting, if hunting was what I wished to do rather than study muskrats.

This feeling of detachment from scientific or professional responsibilities that I tried to cultivate during my earlier hunting trips to Goose Lake did not always seem right for a person of my interests. However, the question in my mind as to whether I should be doing constructive work in the time I was devoting to personal enjoyment on the marsh was answered one chilly fall day in 1942. While

173

I sat in a blind looking off across the cattails and muskrat lodges, I suddenly realized I was in the midst of the heaviest muskrat population that I had ever found. I was not going to pass up the opportunity to learn more about it.

Thus, I added a last major area to those I was keeping under regular observation, and it turned out to be the most important single area on which I worked.

ONE OF THE OWNERS of Goose Lake estimated the muskrat population in the fall of 1942 as about equal to that of the previous fall and winter, when seventeen hundred had actually been taken for fur and about two hundred had escaped unharvested. The 1942 population that so impressed me must have been, therefore, around nineteen hundred. For the south part of the marsh, dominated by massive stands of cattails, the muskrat concentration must have been about thirty-five per acre. Moreover, it was a population that seemed far more secure than I would have expected. Although minks dug into the bank burrows and into the easily accessible lodges of the muskrats on a most conspicuous scale, the muskrats kept their living quarters in good repair, and only about a half dozen mink droppings, from a total of perhaps 125 examined from midautumn to early March, contained muskrat remains.

Fewer than six hundred muskrats were known to have been trapped from that heavy Goose Lake population during the winter of 1942–43. However, the trapping methods used had been selective for the more restless and ill-situated parts of the population, and the removal of these muskrats did much to relieve the social tensions existing as of late fall and early winter. Winter losses from miscellaneous causes (including predation, fighting, and disease) almost certainly did not exceed one hundred. Nor was the food supply ruinously depleted during the winter by the twelve hundred resident muskrats—most of them on about forty acres.

It was when spring came that the build-up in social tensions of the heavy muskrat population reached a boiling-over stage. Hundreds of muskrats moved overland when the ice melted. Muskrats dead of fight wounds could be seen almost anywhere about the marsh. In one day, I examined eleven such victims along a half-mile of shore. More than twenty-five were reported killed by automobile traffic in one week on about a quarter-mile of the main street in Jewell, a town three-quarters of a mile west of Goose Lake in the direction of travel of most of the dispersing muskrats. Of course, many wanderers were killed by predators—though more by farm dogs than by minks.

A population of about three hundred pairs, or about 630 adult muskrats, lived with a fair degree of security for some weeks after the spring dispersal. Although fighting continued between residents of the shore zone and the transients that still circulated there, one deep-marsh tract of six acres had an average of seven and a half pairs per acre crowded together without much visible antagonism. These six acres were part of the most heavily populated twenty acres of the marsh. All together, the twenty acres had an average of six pairs per acre, not including nineteen pairs living in the burrow systems of two small islands situated in the midst of the tract. This was, numerically, the highest breeding density of muskrats so far recorded on a sizeable tract of marsh during the Iowa investigations.

It was an area worth watching, and I watched it. I spent more time on Goose Lake from late spring of 1943 through the fall of 1948 than on all other central Iowa study areas combined.

Even so, I cannot say exactly when in 1943 the population ceased being merely a "saturation" population and became patently top-heavy for its environment, or when its increasingly unhappy situation turned into real crisis. The formerly thriving cattail stand was killed by high water, and by early June the marsh had deteriorated badly. At that time, most of the muskrats were feeding upon a surface covering of duckweed and upon submerged material, including recently killed cattail rootstocks. Later, the muskrats of the shore zone fed upon vegetation growing on shore, as did the occupants of deep-water tracts that could go ashore via routes unimpeded by jealous residents of the shore zone. Still later, large numbers of muskrats visited cornfields and other agricultural lands—an unusual type of behavior for genuinely marsh-dwelling muskrats. One corner of Goose Lake nearest the outlet was the site of a substantial midsummer migration of animals permanently leaving the marsh: a calculated total of about fifty-five adults and 190 young.

Few young were born on the marsh after the middle of June. That much was plain from the field observations alone, and this fact was verified in the fall by the examination of the uteri of forty adult females. Of the forty, five had not conceived young during the breeding season, fourteen had conceived a single litter each, twelve had conceived two litters each, six had conceived three litters each, and three had conceived four litters each. Despite a large average size of nearly eight young per litter, the small average number of litters born per female—an average of less than two, even if we ignore the non-breeders—is itself indicative of great tension.

Of the young that were born many were killed by adults and others stayed alive because of the furtive habits they developed to avoid harrassment by adults. Penalties for unwariness could be drastic. An adult might swim up to a recently weaned young lying on the water eating duckweed, attack it viciously and thoroughly, and matter-of-factly swim away from its body. Minks preyed upon the young muskrats forced ashore from the overpopulated central tracts. There was a mink den on one of the two islands in the midst of the heaviest concentration of muskrats, and twenty-five of 258 mink droppings for late June, July, and August contained remains of young muskrats.

Although the scientific literature had some references to muskrats dying of epidemic disease, the epidemic that gained headway at Goose Lake in the fall of 1943 may have been the first to be studied in detail.

From the observed beginning of the epidemic in August, up to freeze-up in November, it killed about two hundred muskrats at Goose Lake. For these first few months of the epidemic, the disease losses were largely confined to the muskrats of the heavily populated twenty-acre tract centering about the small islands.

(Despite the large amount of work that has since been done on the disease responsible for the epidemic, no one, in my opinion, has satisfactorily demonstrated anywhere nearly as much as we need to know about its cause. It is, however, a disease that is known over much of the geographic range of muskrats in North America, and its principal manifestations are liver lesions and visceral hemorrhages, in varying combinations.)

Other types of mortality were fairly low in relation to the numbers of muskrats present at Goose Lake in the fall of 1943—and such mortality as occurred was due mostly to muskrats killing muskrats or muskrats being killed by minks and dogs on shore. The troubles of the wanderers increased with the approach of freeze-up, and, on November 12, dozens of muskrats behaving like transients were seen traveling across the new ice. Up to this time, the minks had not been getting near the deep-water sites of disease mortality.

From late November to the middle of December, the epidemic spread to all muskrat-occupied parts of Goose Lake, and the population collapsed in a spectacular manner. By mid-December, possibly fifty muskrats were still alive on the marsh, all at places well removed from the vicinity of the islands. By spring, there was no evidence of any survival, whatever, and the trifling numbers present early in the spring of 1944 all could be accounted for as newcomers. The total mortality from the Goose Lake epidemic of the hemorrhagic disease from fall through winter was between one thousand and thirteen hundred muskrats.

As soon as the minks were able to travel on the ice, they began digging into the muskrat lodges in search of disease victims, and half of over two hundred mink droppings deposited from then until mid-March contained muskrat remains.

One thing that this winter's study of minks responding to dead muskrats brought out: the "sign"—the opened lodges, the strewn bits of skin and partly cleaned bones, the heads and feet and tails, the blood smears, the bodies dragged over the snow—all looked like "sign" of predation

by minks, but it was not. Specimens of partly eaten muskrats that were still sufficiently complete to show anything
diagnostic had their disease lesions, and their sexual condition showed that they had died in early winter, though
the minks may not have found or eaten on them until late
winter or spring.

I had seen something like this before in other winters,
and had wondered why well-situated muskrats were being
preyed upon so unexpectedly by minks. I had not seen
much evidence of muskrats dying then, but I really was
not seeing so very much at Goose Lake either, considering
the magnitude of this die-off. Only a small fraction of the
disease victims were dying outside of their lodge and burrow chambers, and most of the dead I did see outside were
in the form of mink-eaten fragments or mink droppings.

On other central Iowa observational areas, mink predation upon muskrats followed expected patterns in 1943.
Until mid-February of that year, the approximately 175
muskrats wintering on Little Wall Lake had gotten along
well, despite the fact that minks had dug into almost every
lodge. Then, 153 of 208 mink droppings from the last half
of February to mid-March contained muskrat remains—
the equivalent of up to ten or twelve individual muskrats.
This period of vulnerability coincided with the beginning
of the spring dispersal, and, after the elimination of what
seemed to have been the vulnerable individuals, muskrat
remains were found in only five of sixty-nine mink droppings for the second half of March.

During the summer of 1943, the sixty-five pairs of
muskrats at Little Wall Lake had a most productive breeding season—quite in contrast to the one at neighboring
Goose Lake. The entire marsh was again habitable for
muskrats after years of drought and, by late fall, it had a
population of about thirteen hundred, mostly—but not all
—well-situated animals.

Of the thirteen hundred, entering the winter of 1943–
44, about ninety were animals of such restless habits that
they frequently came out on the surface of the ice, and I
judged that they were newcomers to the marsh. My guess
was that many had come from neighboring Goose Lake as

a result of the population crisis there, but muskrats from other sources were also in circulation about the countryside. The restless ones were preyed upon by the dozen or more minks wintering at Little Wall Lake, and the more conspicuous the restlessness became the greater the predation it drew. Then after elimination of the restless part of the population, the others lived securely, although the minks continually dug into their lodges. Perhaps twelve hundred muskrats survived the winter.

LITTLE WALL LAKE was, in 1944, the site of a muskrat crisis similar to the one at Goose Lake the previous year: there was a large spring breeding population, high water killed a splendid cattail stand, and muskrats found themselves in increasingly desperate circumstances from midsummer to fall. As a result, most adult female muskrats gave birth to their last litters of the season by mid-June, killing of young by older animals became conspicuous, and the muskrats of entire tracts of marsh went to shore to raid adjacent cornfields or to abandon the marsh completely. The mink population consisted of a female with her litter of young and an estimated two or three adult males.

For one deep-water group of muskrats a windstorm in July made a hard situation even worse: lodges were washed apart and their occupants were marooned on shore near a den where the mother mink kept her litter of young. Bodies of sixteen young muskrats appeared in the prey debris outside of the den, and, of 149 mink droppings deposited outside of the den in early July, twenty-two contained muskrat remains that could be fairly well dated to the time of the storm or shortly after. Prior to the storm, only one of eighty-five droppings for May and June had contained muskrat remains, for, despite the savagery of muskrat-to-muskrat relationships out in the marsh during June, this was still before many newly weaned young were reaching places where they could be exploited by the minks.

Big shoreward movements of the muskrats began in

mid-July and the minks responded. They were not, however, the only responsive predators. Foxes, dogs, and large birds of prey also responded to muskrats sitting in the open with fight wounds, to muskrats living in holes on hillsides and under tree roots, or to muskrats wandering off across pastures and stubble fields.

Throughout the summer of 1944, I kept close watch at Little Wall Lake for evidence of the hemorrhagic disease that had swept Goose Lake. In late summer and early fall, I found some animals suspiciously dead at one place along the west-central shore, but these were too decayed for satisfactory examination. The first clearly diagnosed disease victim was found near there in October. During the next two weeks, twenty-one more dead were found, all of them along a seventy-yard stretch of shore including the original focus of infection. The minks learned about this focus as soon as I did.

The original focus of infection appeared to be devoid of living muskrats by November. By the opening of the trapping season on November 10, the epidemic had depopulated nearly three-quarters of a mile of shore zone, killing about 350 muskrats. The fur trapping eliminated both the local mink population and about fourteen hundred of the muskrats.

In late January, 1945, a mink appeared on Little Wall Lake and stationed itself along the stretch of shore where the 350 muskrats had died in late fall. It subsisted in part upon dead muskrats in the burrows but fed mostly on fishes, and as a result only two of its first thirty-six droppings examined contained muskrat remains. Thereafter, it discovered a place where an estimated seventy-five to one hundred muskrats had died from the hemorrhagic disease in late November or early December. Forty of fifty-eight mink droppings from this place—with its greater availability of refrigerated muskrat flesh—contained muskrat remains.

DURING THE FOLLOWING YEARS, studies of muskrat populations on central Iowa areas were continued. Muskrats were observed over and over again adjusting to both favorable and unfavorable environmental conditions. Many of the field notes relate to places where muskrats died from hemorrhagic disease, fought among themselves, wandered cross-country, and fed predators and scavengers. There continued to be a close relation between mortality from hemorrhagic disease and unusually large percentages of mink droppings containing muskrat remains.

A case history of a somewhat unusual nature was recorded for Goose Lake during one winter. As of mid-December, about sixty muskrats were still alive on the marsh after a fall epidemic had subsided, and these lived with some security until a rain and thaw in early January flooded many of them out of their subsurface retreats. Minks killed at least seven at this time, and twenty of twenty-one droppings contained muskrat remains, compared with one in thirty-two droppings that had been deposited shortly before the emergency.

One especially detailed study of predatory responses during a drought crisis was made at Goose Lake in 1947. There, the marsh had sixteen breeding territories in June, a peak population of 180 muskrats by mid-July, fewer than seventy on the entire marsh by October and no muskrats at all by the following spring.

Effects of the drought were felt as early as late July. As the shallower parts of the marsh dried up, the family groups that could move into deeper water unimpeded by territories of other muskrats did so. Occupants of territories that were blocked off from deeper parts by the presence of other territories tended to stay where they were or to leave the marsh as cross-country wanderers. One of the wanderers was a young animal found dead of the hemorrhagic disease, September 15, on the shore of Little Wall Lake, three miles from where it had been tagged at Goose Lake in early summer.

Six young muskrats were known to have been killed by horned owls during the drought exposure. At least five drought-exposed dead were fed upon by minks, though I could not determine whether they had been killed by the minks. Three muskrats were dug out of a dry lodge and killed by farm dogs at a time when other occupants of the lodge were dying from the hemorrhagic disease. My field notes refer to the mortality of forty-seven muskrats (including twenty clearly dying from the hemorrhagic disease) from the onset of the drought through November, 1947.

One freeze-out crisis—this, too, at Goose Lake—was especially dramatic. About sixty muskrats entered the winter on a still wet but food-poor part of the lake, there to winter securely until late January, despite intrusions into their lodges by minks. When cold weather froze the water to the bottom and sealed practically the entire food supply of these muskrats in the ice, their status changed from one of relative comfort to one of overwhelming crisis in less than a week. Three weeks later not a muskrat was alive on the marsh. Forty mink droppings examined during the last three weeks of February contained muskrat remains in all except two, and twenty contemporaneous mink victims were recorded in the field notes.

The above crisis was studied almost according to a day-by-day schedule. As the ice cut off their food supply, the muskrats came out of their lodges to search for food on top of the ice. They ate upon the bodies of fishes frozen into plunge holes of the lodges; they ate the insides of their lodges as high up as they could reach; they ate on the dry and frozen tops of lodges from the outside; they journeyed back and forth between lodges and the weedy growths on shore. Four were known to have abandoned the marsh and others doubtless did also. Another was found on the ice in dying condition, eyes frozen. One muskrat escaped injured from an encounter with a mink, only to be devoured by its fellow muskrats soon afterward.

The muskrats tracked up the snow all around the lodges, and the minks made tracks too as they dragged bodies off to their retreats on shore. The minks were the final agencies of much of the mortality but their predation made no difference in the end. The muskrats did not have a chance to survive, minks or no minks, once things went drastically wrong for them.

FOLLOWING THE LOSS OF extensive cattail growths from high water in 1944, Little Wall Lake was left for many years with a greatly reduced capacity for accommodating muskrats. However, for most winters of the investigation thereafter, the few hundreds of animals entering each winter usually got along well—so well in fact that any evidence of mortality became something to study carefully.

I remember telling a game warden friend about finding muskrat remains in five out of nine early winter mink droppings gathered from one corner of a marsh at a time when the population of about 250 muskrats was otherwise wintering securely. I expressed the thought that I would find a disease focus there in the spring. When the ice melted, I picked up six dead. From their stages of sexual maturity, death could be dated to the time of appearance of the muskrat remains in the mink droppings. None of the six had been eaten upon, and the four that were in suitable condition to examine for disease lesions were proven victims. Dying of muskrats occurred at this same disease focus during the next two years and each time mink droppings reflected the muskrat mortality.

One case history from Wall Lake illustrates further the type of evidence that kept showing up, once the studies got down to really detailed analysis.

The first indication of dying in this case was the occurrence of muskrat remains in seven of sixteen mink droppings examined during the first half of March from a little group of lodges. A large lodge had an unrepaired mink hole and muskrat remains outside. A few days later, remains of three other muskrats were found. One of these was of a disease victim fed upon by a mink in a neighboring small lodge and another was of a sick muskrat that had come out on the ice, was overtaken by the mink, killed, and cached in a snowdrift. A graduate student and I put in a heavy half-day of work with an ax, and we opened sixteen frozen lodges in the center of the suspected focus. We found a total of nine dead, of which five were sufficiently intact to show characteristic lesions of the hemorrhagic disease. In one case we cut around the base of an enormous lodge until the top came loose, and then we strained to lift it up like a great lid; as we lifted, we saw three muskrats huddled together as if asleep beside a frozen plunge hole. The mink had not yet gotten to their bodies.

A FEW YEARS AGO, I tried to summarize what had been learned about mink-muskrat relationships since the publication in 1943 of my bulletin, *An Analysis of Mink Predation Upon Muskrats in North-Central United States.*

The total of 13,176 mink droppings examined from central and north-central Iowa areas during this interval included 2,415 containing muskrat remains. Between sixteen and seventeen hundred (65 and 70 per cent) of the 2,415 muskrat-containing droppings were judged on good evidence to have resulted from exploitation of diseased muskrats, mainly simple scavenging.

A total of 674, or 28 per cent, of the 2,415 droppings could be assigned to the different categories of mink predation upon muskrats. Of the 674, about 360 were made up of remains of muskrats that had been vulnerable to minks chiefly because of their troubles with other muskrats. These victims were of all ages, sizes, and physical conditions. The muskrat remains in about one hundred more of the droppings were of predation victims that had been made vulnerable by acute drought exposures and freeze-out crises. Most of the other muskrat representations, or about 210, were of young muskrats caught by the minks under varying conditions of disadvantage.

Of course, among the victims represented by these droppings, there could well have been an occasional one that got killed and eaten by a mink because it was unlucky at the moment or did not do the right thing, but the old generalization was still valid: Muskrats living in suitable habitat and within the limits of crowding that they themselves found tolerable were not much preyed upon by minks.

RACCOON

RACCOONS OFTEN RESPOND to the availability of dead or helpless muskrats much as minks do. In areas having severe disease losses, the raccoons sometimes have given me so much competition for the dead muskrats that I have had trouble finding what I needed for examination. Sometimes about the only dead I could find would be those dying just before I came along or those that died in places out of reach of the raccoons.

There could be more to exploitation by the raccoons than mere scavenging. During one late winter and early spring the raccoons were much interested in a disease focus at Wall Lake. They dug into some of the flimsier lodges and continued visiting this tract until the middle of the spring. Seventeen of sixty raccoon droppings deposited in or near the disease focus from late March to early May contained remains of dozens of young muskrats, their tiny bones sometimes packed throughout the droppings. The tops of the muskrat lodges within the focus—but not outside of it—showed evidence of raccoons raiding the nests in which helpless young muskrats were kept. After early May the exploitation of young muskrats at this focus ceased, and the raccoons began working on another.

From late March to early June that same year I hastily examined approximately one thousand raccoon droppings from muskrat-filled shallows of other parts of Wall Lake but without noting muskrat remains in any of them. In the summer and fall, another one thousand raccoon droppings from dry and drying parts of the marsh contained muskrat remains in six, and all of these six were from the vicinities of known foci of the hemorrhagic disease.

Also, one of the foci that had so conspicuously drawn attention of the raccoons in 1953 had a history of deadliness that could be traced back—not always with complete certainty—at least to the early forties. In 1947, the field notes showed, this had been the one place on the marsh where raccoon predation upon helpless young muskrats in lodge nests had occurred to any obvious degree.

The possible connection between epidemic disease of muskrats and predation by raccoons upon young muskrats was not ideally proven. In its rough outlines, it looked like this: The raccoons were first attracted to disease foci by the presence of dead muskrats and, as the raccoons dug into lodges after the dead, they discovered nests containing living and very available young muskrats. Thereafter, while working such areas, they deliberately searched for helpless litters in the lodges that they could conveniently reach—that is, those in the shallow water zones.

I do not know why the raccoons did not extend their nest-raiding tactics to shallow-water muskrat habitats outside of the disease foci after learning to hunt in this way. Maybe they did, but if so, I could not often find evidence of their feeding upon muskrats—whether young or old, healthy or sick or dead—that were very far outside of well-known disease foci. Nor was it a matter of not having opportunities to study food habits of raccoons. During the years of muskrat abundance on Wall and Goose lakes, raccoon droppings could be found there by the thousands. Sometimes, muskrat lodges would be heaped with raccoon droppings full of crayfish remains, or corn. Occasionally they would have plum pits, duck or coot or pheasant or blackbird feathers, or rabbit or mouse or pocket gopher fur, but usually they had nothing of muskrat in them.

IN CONCLUDING THIS two-chapter discussion of predation and muskrats, I think of what is still unknown in muskrat-predator interrelationships:

Many of the unknowns are of rather small details. What goes on during an encounter between a mink and a muskrat inside of a muskrat lodge, or in the air spaces under the ice? What makes the difference between a muskrat escaping a mink or a mink capturing a muskrat, when the margin of success of one effort or the other may be slight? Why is it that litters of helpless young muskrats may at times be raised without losses practically under the noses of minks? Why are some muskrats able to take care of themselves against enemies during emergencies while others are not? Why may a little water in the entrance of a drought-exposed burrow confer protection against minks that is out of all proportion to its volume or to the surface it covers? These are but a few of the interesting questions that arise.

Among the greater hindrances to our understanding of population dynamics of the muskrats—and, accordingly, to our attempts to appraise population effects of predation—have been the unknowns associated with muskrat movements after the breeding season.

It was not until the last decade of the central Iowa field studies that I got any clear idea of the magnitude of the orderly adjustments that could occur along the streams in late summer and early fall. These orderly adjustments (which should not be confused with cross-country wandering of desperate muskrats) were then observed to occur along the whole length of small and medium-sized creeks and were much in contrast with the sedentary behavior of marsh-dwelling muskrats that spent their lives within small areas—within areas of only a few acres in many cases. Along Squaw Creek, adjustments were traced for at least

fifteen miles, and they almost certainly extended for substantially greater distances when the migrants had inviting
travel routes and nothing better to attract them to stay
than the kinds of places they had already abandoned.
Contrasting with the above pattern of adjustments, muskrats had wintered in numbers as high as forty to sixty per
mile along these same creeks in the earlier years of the
Iowa muskrat investigations—sometimes despite considerable drought exposure.

These year-to-year variations in behavior of the muskrats may have a pronounced bearing upon local vulnerability to predation, especially to the extent that they result in much movement in strange places and delays or
failures in finding suitable wintering quarters. But, compensations may work throughout these variations, too.
The late-summer and fall adjustments look more and more
like mechanisms underlying the observed tendencies of
muskrat populations of the larger land units (or combinations of units) to conform to mathematical patterns—to
balance and counterbalance and fit together with a wholeness that cancels out the smaller details.

The central Iowa data from the twenty-three square
miles kept under regular observation from 1941 through
1956 will serve as an example. I shall not give the figures
for the stream-dwelling populations occupying a total of
twenty square miles during the above study period, but
the reader may be assured that the ups and downs of the
populations and the responsiveness of the muskrats to
weather, to environmental conditions, and to population
densities of their own kind occurred in a highly irregular
manner. I am willing to say that the population data for
most years are characterized by their nonconformity to
patterns, as long as stream data alone are considered. However, when stream and marsh populations are considered
together, for the total area of twenty-three square miles
for which the most accurate central Iowa data exist, patterns emerge suggesting that the density of the breeding
population determines population growth—always, of
course, in reference to environmental conditions.

The central Iowa muskrat data emphasize another

basic fact learned during the quail studies: Before we can expect to appraise population effects of anything suspected of being a limiting factor (including predation), we could well make sure that we are working with populations living on land units that are adequate to bring out any existing patterns.

Wall Lake, because of its relative isolation from other muskrat habitats, usually had the most self-contained muskrat population of any of the regularly observed Iowa study areas. The fall populations at Wall Lake during our years of records had a tendency to level off at about ten muskrats per acre of marsh having water covering the bottom. Whatever it may signify in detailed analysis, this tendency held up fairly well despite tremendous annual variations in kinds and numbers of locally resident predators that liked muskrat flesh.

IT MAY BE RECALLED that the data for both quail and muskrats seemed to show many peculiarities for 1936 (and to some extent for 1937), at about the same time that the ruffed grouse and snowshoe hares of the northern Lake States reached one of their "cyclic lows." Insofar as the years for minimal populations of these grouse and hares had been coming at average intervals of about a decade, I made special efforts to see what, if anything, might be different on my muskrat areas between 1945 and 1947. What I actually saw during my field work of the latter years disappointed me at the time. It was, in fact, quite apparent that the population fluctuations of muskrats on our Iowa study areas were not showing much agreement with the fluctuations of the grouse and hares.

I did see, however, in both 1936 and 1946 that the muskrats showed conspicuously greater inclination to abandon attractive-looking territories or home ranges and to go wandering about the countryside than they had in other years. To my eyes the muskrats had, in the summer and fall of 1946, above-average food, water, and cover conditions, yet the animals abandoned central Iowa streams, to wander cross-country on a grand scale, without any reason that I could imagine at the time. Large numbers of muskrats were killed by highway traffic. About three hundred moved into Little Wall Lake and established themselves in the central part—which then had very few animals that could have been called true residents. About one hundred more moved into Goose Lake, which had been depopulated in midsummer by an epidemic of the hemorrhagic disease. These cross-country movements of 1946 were quite exceptional in their magnitude and should not be considered in the same category as the more usual upstream and downstream adjustments.

Another, though probably related, behavioristic trait that was traced through the pages of notes and tabulations was the greater intolerance that muskrats showed toward crowding by their own kind during the 1935–37 and 1945–47 periods, compared with the 1941–43 period. The data on territorial distribution indicated that in the breeding season adult muskrats tolerated at least twice as many territories per unit of area in first-class cattail or bulrush marshes during the 1941–43 year-grouping than during either the 1935–37 or 1945–47 groupings. During the "cyclic lows" represented by the latter year-groupings, there was much friction, and the maximum breeding densities leveled off at about three pairs per acre. Also, the local populations tended to distribute themselves with a fair amount of uniformity over whole marshes in strong and poor environment alike. During the 1941–43 "cyclic high," the muskrats were sufficiently tolerant of crowding to allow up to six to eight pairs per acre in the better parts of marshes, while leaving the poorer parts sparsely populated. In other words, muskrats living under comparable conditions seemed to show much more of what could be called a calm and steady outlook on life and were more tolerant and adaptable, generally, during the "cyclic high" than during the "cyclic low" year-groupings.

The thought came to me along about 1947, I believe, that what I had been seeing in the way of "cyclic symptoms" during especially 1936 and 1946 might have resulted from a kind of mass exhaustion, and that idea still does not seem unreasonable.

The data on fecundity of muskrats resulting from an examination of 4,785 female muskrats indicate that variations in physiology were linked with cycles. During many years of the study, a certain per cent of the young females born conceived young during the calendar year of their own birth; but such precocity in breeding tended to be lacking during the years of or centering about the chronological "cyclic lows" of 1936, 1946, and 1956.

Another correlation was found between cyclic phase and size of litter. We have data on 2,656 litters born to or conceived by adult females, and during the "cyclic low" years the litters were of minimal sizes, averaging 6.4 young per litter. In contrast, the mean litter sizes were 8.2 for both 1941 and 1951, the years coming halfway between the three "low-cycle" years.

Other data that fit—so far as they go—the concept that year-to-year changes in the physiology of the muskrats may follow something like a ten-year periodicity are those obtained on the hemorrhagic disease after intensive studies were begun in 1943.

It was not that mortality from the disease was necessarily higher during the "cyclic lows" than during other year-groupings. The dying of about eighty-five hundred muskrats on our Iowa study areas during a fifteen-year period was by no means restricted to "cyclic lows." More muskrats by far died on the areas in 1943–44 than in 1945–47 and 1955–57. The chances of an individual or a part of a local population contracting the disease did vary with time and place but not in any way that seemed to have "cyclic" connections. Not even the greater wandering tendencies of the animals in 1946 seemed to result in more widespread dying.

Nevertheless, the hemorrhagic lesions in 498 especially informative disease victims were of types suggesting lengths of time that they had been able to stay alive after becoming infected. The notes resulting from these post-mortems provide the basis for distinguishing between inferior, intermediate, and superior resistance.

The years of inferior resistance to the disease were the years of low fecundity—and, conversely, the years of superior resistance were the years of high fecundity. This could hardly have been due merely to chance. Nor do I think that chance could explain the differing degrees of social tolerance, restlessness, and so on.

We are a long way from understanding what is behind the "cyclic" changes in muskrat physiology, and we also lack any very complete understanding as to how much they may influence predation upon the muskrats. We can feel reasonably sure, however, that the physiological changes do have their influence on the kind and amount and perhaps the population significance of predation upon the muskrats. Whether we label any factor "cyclic" or give it another name; whether our unknowns ultimately prove to be climatic or environmental changes, solar radiation, or factors still unguessed; or whether they are never satisfactorily explained, we are entitled to conclude the following: At the very least, anything can be expected to increase vulnerability of muskrat populations to predation if it decreases their social tolerance and hence the effective carrying capacity of the places in which they are adapted to live.

11

INDICATIONS AND TRENDS

I CANNOT SAY with any comfortable assurance how much the findings on predator-prey relationships already discussed in this book may apply to other animal populations. Nevertheless, there are indications that the population dynamics of many birds and mammals have their similarities to those of the quail, muskrats, pheasants, grouse, and the waterfowl.

Without committing ourselves to any particularly sweeping thesis as to predator-prey relationships in other forms, we may properly look for any trends the evidence may show.

THE BARN RAT (also called the brown or Norway rat) may be heavily preyed upon by owls and certain other predators in some north-central localities. So far as my own observations show, this predation tends to be centered upon individuals or parts of populations forced to live at a disadvantage.

Rats may overflow good environment into inhospitable environment. They may get started wandering into strange places, sometimes in conspicuous overland movements. They may be caught by cold weather or snow in food-poor places and forced to resort to hazardous routines

HORNED OWL

to stay alive—and they are not well adapted to withstand extremes of hunger and cold.

The Norway rat may show toleration of crowding—Harold Gunderson[37] reported the poisoning of more than four thousand on three acres about a set of Iowa farm buildings during a thirty-day experiment in rat control. Nevertheless, the rat can also show much intolerance of crowding. As a result the social frictions and unrest of crowded rat populations of town dumps, slaughter houses, and such places may invite the attention of rat-hunting predators that frequent such places, even if the great abundance of rats alone did not especially attract predators.

Rat remains were found in 5 per cent of nearly four thousand cold-weather horned owl pellets examined from my north-central study areas and in 9 per cent of nearly a thousand from late spring, summer, and fall. Up to 70 per cent of some fair-sized lots contained rat remains. In four of five cases of the heaviest predation by horned owls, the owls patently got most of their rats from farm land or from the vicinity of farm buildings. In the fifth case, the owls preyed upon the rats of a southern Wisconsin lake shore.

It was also plain from miscellaneous sources of north-central data that barred owls, foxes, minks, and almost any predators of similar prowess might be expected to kill rats from time to time, according to their opportunities.

I cannot see that any of this predation could have had limiting effects on rat populations unless it served to make the less favorable living places completely uninhabitable for rats. Under most conditions observed during at least the months of snow, the field-living rats killed by predators could not have been expected to have wintered where they were anyway; but some individuals or groups of individuals occupying isolated corncribs or corn shocks were not only well fed but were, apparently, also withstanding the cold up to the time of their elimination by predators. In these latter cases, the restless behavior of the rats, as betrayed by their running back and forth between corn shocks or by seemingly pointless journeys out away from the corncribs, clearly predisposed them to predation by watchful birds of prey.

There is always the question of how significant predation by small-bodied though formidable predators may be to rat populations, even to those living in choice environments. Weasels and large snakes able to go into rat holes would seem to constitute a most special problem for rats. W. D. Crabb's[38] study of spotted skunks on southeast Iowa farms brought out instances as extreme as rats disappearing from premises after a spotted skunk took up residence—as well as instances of rats and spotted skunks living together under the same buildings and wood piles. Crabb found big seasonal differences in spotted skunk predation upon the rats with predation heaviest in the winter and spring.

I am not sure there is compensatory significance in the fact that spotted skunk predation on rats was lighter at seasons when horned owl predation was heavier, but the data on rat populations obtained by D. E. Davis, J. T. Emlen, J. B. Calhoun, and colleagues[39] in their exhaustive studies at Baltimore do show much in the way of compensatory trends. As in the case of Iowa muskrats, the population levels of the Baltimore rats were determined primarily by the social tolerance of the rats in relation to their habitats, with rates of gain decreasing as the population became crowded. Predation by cats and dogs had no apparent effect on established rat populations, though the presence of cats and dogs possibly prevented invasion and establishment of rats in new areas.

The Baltimore rat populations were subjected to experimental manipulation. Introduction of strange rats increased social tensions, and this resulted in increased mortality among strangers and residents alike and in upsets in breeding patterns. When populations were reduced 50 to 90 per cent by poisoning, their recovery rates were higher than for populations that were only slightly reduced. The growth curves of the populations following the poisoning were of a type suggesting a great deal of self-limitation.

There have been times when I thought that field-living rats in the north-central region showed some lack of

racial adaptations to take care of themselves against native
north-central predators, and this could be true. Nevertheless, the defensive prowess of a rat in relation to its size
must be advantageous to it in the event of attack by one
of the many predators best able to go where the rats themselves go. Considering how viciously a strong rat can bite,
and its commonly observed courage of desperation, I can
understand how even a weasel may not necessarily have
its own way down there in a rat hole out of human sight.

J. M. LINSDALE, [40] IN reporting the results of a long-term
and most detailed study of the California ground squirrel,
cited examples indicating that one effect of artificial
reduction of the ground squirrel population was to
increase the rate at which the survivors produced young.
He found a close correlation between numbers of the
ground squirrels and the quality of their environment.
On his study area (Hastings Natural History Reservation
in Monterey County, California) the species was known
to decrease and disappear on tracts no longer used for livestock grazing or human cultivation. In his treatment of
predation, he felt that the bobcat was capable of exerting
a major influence on numbers of the ground squirrels on
his area.

F. C. Evans and Robert Holdenreid[41] studied the same
species of ground squirrel on another California area during two full breeding seasons in the early forties. They
recorded April-to-September gains of 136 per cent from a
marked population of thirty-six on an 8.2-acre tract in
1940 and 109 per cent from fifty-four in 1941. So far, the
lowering of the rate of gain as the breeding population increased looks about as one might expect, but the data obtained partly through the breeding season of 1942 showed
an actual loss between April and July—a decline to twenty-
six animals from the forty-four present in April. The
authors attributed this decline to heavy losses among the
animals born in 1941. Although they did not account for
the loss in detail, bubonic plague was found in fleas collected from the ground squirrels in June, 1942, whereas

no evidence of the disease had been observed in the two other years.

In Michigan, D. L. Allen's[42] investigation of fox squirrels showed that small breeding stocks were consistently more productive of young, proportionally, than were large stocks. He emphasized the importance of environmental conditions in governing population levels of the squirrels. And, it seems to me, this is just about the pattern indicated by what scattered and fragmentary information we have on other members of the squirrel family, from chipmunks to woodchucks. A certain amount of compensatory gain can be an expected response to losses of unusual severity.

THE POPULATION DYNAMICS of north-central rabbits and mice have their features in common with those of the muskrats and the other species of animals that have been intensively studied. Rabbits and mice also require suitable environment in which to thrive, and their seasonal rates of gain and loss can conform to patterns that look rather definite for a given area at a given time. Much evidence suggests that predation upon rabbits and mice can be centered upon overproduced, badly situated, or otherwise vulnerable parts of populations at the same times that other parts of the populations live with apparent security.

My feeling is that the main differences in the operation of the natural laws governing populations of the rabbits and mice and the quail and muskrats relate to the social tolerances of the species and the intensities of the predation suffered. While quail wintering on the north-central study areas would need to be highly vulnerable to suffer predation exceeding 25 to 30 per cent per ninety days, and heavy muskrat populations may get along from late summer to spring suffering almost no losses from predation, the rabbit and mouse populations may still be preyed upon until their numbers are reduced to a small fraction of what they were during the most populous part of a year. This view fits in with the known facts that the rabbits and mice do serve as staple prey for many predators, at all seasons of the year, and that, even as staple prey, they do have ability to take care of themselves with considerable security once their numbers are down to certain levels with respect to the capacities of their environments to accommodate them.

Still, I am most reluctant to attempt the broader generalizations concerning either the rabbits or the mice as prey animals. In the literature are descriptions of predatory exploitation of mouse populations so severe as to be virtually annihilative on a local scale—especially when the exploiters were weasels able to pursue the mice in burrow systems. But I keep returning unsatisfied to a concept held by at least some of the leading students of predation upon mouse populations: that the predation takes the form of a steady attrition, whittling away week after week and month after month, always tending to push the population downward.

I do not intend to be so brash as to say what happens in mouse populations on the basis of my muskrat work, but it should be proper to point up a distinction that came out of the muskrat work.

The peak year for Iowa muskrats, 1943, was the one year when the losses through predation could have been thought of as representing a steady month-by-month attrition. It was the one year of my intensive field studies when I felt no surprise at finding muskrats showing up in predator diets at any time, anywhere. The muskrats were then living or trying to live in almost all of the wet places in the state and in some places that were not even wet; and the predation upon them seemed most nearly to conform to what I would call the prevailing concepts of predation upon mice.

But the predation suffered by the 1943 muskrat populations was neither random nor in direct proportion to existing populations. Nor was it, according to my interpretation, a primary limiting or regulating factor in the population dynamics of the muskrats. I should say that the limitations of the available environment for the muskrats, in combination with the psychological limitations of the muskrats themselves, comprised the real limiting factor. The ill-situated parts of the 1943 population could not maintain themselves indefinitely, whether their existence was terminated by predation, disease, cold, hunger, or motor traffic. What were obviously the better-situated parts of populations continued to show notable security from wild predators. High thresholds of security of the muskrats could be distinguished in 1943 as well as in less populous years.

In analysis, the predation suffered by the Iowa muskrats in 1943 turned out to be of the familiar types, despite their superficial resemblance to steady attrition. During the breeding months, and for a few weeks after weaning, there was often much wastage of immature animals. Predation, strife between the muskrats themselves, wandering in inhospitable places were all agencies of mortality of the overproduced or vulnerable young. When the biological shaking down was over, the rest of a local population could enjoy a remarkable degree of security from predatory enemies for months—unless it became drought-exposed, evicted, or something else went very much wrong. There was resemblance in 1943 to steady attrition because large numbers of muskrats occupied so many different grades of environment and were subject to so much trouble locally that predators could find some vulnerable muskrats at almost any time.

When we come to the question of possible competitive relationships between mouse species, we have some of the best leads in the extremely detailed studies of T. T. McCabe and Barbara Blanchard[43] on an area near Berkeley, California. They recorded a spectacular example of sweeping predation by weasels upon a local mouse population, and on the basis of this, recognized that predation could have great potential significance; yet they also pointed out in contrast the numerical stability of a mouse population living with singular freedom from "such obvious and more or less accidental agencies."

They found that the three species of deer mice with which they worked showed an extreme sense of environmental specificity—these species tended to segregate into "niches" in a remarkable manner. While the differences between "niches" for one species and another might be too subtle for the human eye to recognize, the different species of mice could recognize them. Each species was closely adjusted to some parts of the terrain and not to others. The advantage that a mouse should gain in competitive relationships and in taking care of itself against predatory enemies through living exactly where it belonged would certainly be one of the big factors regulating populations of its kind.

McCabe and Blanchard further emphasized the importance of diversity of the environment on population levels of their deer mice. They felt that diversity would continually provide obstacles to the population growth of a single species of mouse. With a perfectly uniform environment, there would be no obstacle of this class to hinder "indefinite expansion, to the point of self-destruction, of a perfectly adapted organism."

The latter concept fits in well with what Fritz Frank[44] found in an exhaustive study of the short-tailed vole, a European counterpart of our American meadow mouse. All "plague districts"—those noted for the extremes of their vole fluctuations—that he studied were represented by large, open, monotonous, and uniform types of vole environment. These places were what the Germans called "cultivation steppes," which were the result of human land use in once-wooded or once-marshy areas of central Europe. Despite differences in geological formation, the uniform structure of the present day landscape was considered by Frank as one of the main features promoting alternately excessive increases followed by population collapses of the voles.

Such violent fluctuations on the part of staple prey animals can be expected to have their repercussions on predator-prey relationships, and some of the most "classic" examples are afforded by meadow mice and snowshoe hares in North America. The average length of the "cycle"—that is, a complete round from peak to peak or from bottom to bottom of a year-to-year fluctuation—is about ten years for the snowshoe hares, compared with an average length of three or four years for the meadow mice.

At their lowest levels, hardly any individuals may remain over the same tracts of land previously having hundreds or thousands, but most of the year-to-year fluctuations are less extreme.

Even though there is much that we do not know about these "cyclic" fluctuations of staple prey groups, I cannot see that predation either prevents rises of the prey to top-heavy abundances or is the primary cause of the declines. When these species reach abundances that are patently excessive, two additional conclusions are justifiable: (1) that the food supply (or some other essential feature) of the environment is good enough to allow a great increase; (2) that the natural intolerances or self-limiting tendencies of the species fail to keep down the increasing population.

No one should expect North American deer to have the variety and numbers of predatory enemies that the rabbits and mice have. Not every flesh-eater that might wish to can kill a deer, but the cougars and timber wolves can be specialists, and, in the absence of the cougars and wolves, a whole array of lesser predators can substitute for the specialists. Bobcats, lynxes, coyotes, and the stronger domestic dogs may prey upon handicapped deer—occasionally on an animal that does not seem to have any perceptible handicap. Young fawns may also be preyed upon by enemies of still smaller sizes (eagles, foxes, medium-small dogs, among others) when handicapped or vulnerable because of overpopulation crises or unsuitable environment. F. Fraser Darling[45] reported very heavy fox predation upon the fawns of the red deer (related to but smaller than our North American elk) in Scotland, where wolves and the larger wild flesh-eaters were exterminated long ago.

The white-tailed deer is the one species of hoofed game with which I have had personal experience. It has its own territorial intolerances and its populations show tendencies toward self-limitation, as by decreased reproductive rates with increased crowding. Such self-limiting tendencies, however, are not strong enough to prevent the

deer from becoming so numerous in the northern Lake
States that they may become stunted and die of starvation
by the thousands.

Overpopulations of deer usually have plenty to eat in
summer, but the few kinds of plants suitable for their
winter staples may be quite restricted in distribution and
quantity. Moreover, the whitetails of our Lake States have
behavior traits that can make bad problems of overpopulation worse. Through their habit of congregating on favored winter range, they may not only wreck the carrying
capacity of the range for themselves but also dominate the
ecology of the overgrazed area. One who has seen a "deer
line" in a deer-filled part of a forest (where everything
more or less edible for deer is eaten as far up as the larger
deer can reach) should have no difficulty in understanding that overpopulations of deer have an impact on other
kinds of life that belong in a forest, too.

A view widely held among biologists and conserva-
tionists is that the deer increase to top-heavy and destructive levels of abundance primarily because they are relieved of pressure from the formidable enemies—particularly the large wolves that preyed upon them when the
white man came. The histories of "deer problem" areas
over various parts of the United States have shown sequences that look as if they must have been due to more
than coincidence. Too often a deer problem has followed
elimination of the local wolves or cougars, especially when
combined with overly strict protection of the deer against
human hunters. Further suggestive is the fact that so
many of the North American areas still having deer populations in good balance with their habitats are in those
regions of Canada and Mexico where the native predators
have been least disturbed by human intervention. The
inclusion of Indians armed with primitive weapons along
with wolves and cougars as native predators upon deer
should not make any appreciable difference in our conclusions regarding population effects upon deer of the
more formidable of deer-killing predators.

Irrespective of what we find with other species more
self-limited by social intolerances, it does look as if deer

populations need predation (or its functional equivalent—human hunting) as a regulating factor, for the well-being of deer populations and deer range. But this is an overly simple disposal of the intricate subject of predation upon deer. We need to go further.

The population status of whitetails in the north-central region has been tremendously affected by the environmental changes of the last half-century. Unquestionably, one of the aftermaths of the wholesale logging in the northern Lake States early in the century was the improvement of vast areas of formerly poor or mediocre deer range. Shrubs and young trees rather than mature forests are what made "deer country." Without implying that we should let forest fires burn uncontrolled or go back to wasteful "Paul Bunyan" methods of logging, I may point out that effective fire protection and management for timber production are now gradually making the once vast areas of second-growth woods less habitable for the deer. At the same time, the deer have either found improved conditions or adapted themselves better to living in the north-central prairie states, for they have become abundant in many parts of agricultural Iowa, Nebraska, and the Dakotas that had no deer thirty years ago.

I do not pretend to know what else should be considered besides predation and plant succession, human hunting and land use, and behavior of the deer. Climate, soil fertility, disease, competition with other plant-eaters are all in the equation somewhere, but perhaps not operating in ways that we would think logical.

In my opinion, the man best qualified to appraise the population significance of predation upon deer is A. Starker Leopold,[46] who has long studied black-tailed deer in the Southwest under conditions ranging from the highly artificialized to the virtually primitive. He and his colleagues found that the deer thrived where conditions were right, and that the presence of predators had comparatively little effect on the size of the deer population. He concluded that the factor primarily limiting deer populations in areas of his familiarity was food, and that predation losses tended to be borne by the surplus animals.

In the above respects, the rather incidental nature of the predation upon deer seems to parallel that of the predation upon the quail and the muskrats with which I have worked. The main difference that I see is in what happens in the absence of what might be called normal predation: The deer, with their less effective self-limiting intolerances, can increase up to excessive and self-destructive abundance peaks incomparably more than may be expected for species having the stronger intolerances that arrest further increases short of Life's "last resort" check, insufficiency of food.

The writings of C. H. D. Clarke,[47] A. W. F. Banfield,[48] Francis Harper,[49] A. Starker Leopold, and F. Fraser Darling[50] afford, I should say, a reasonably clear picture of wolf-caribou relationships. The wolves can be the chief predatory enemies of the caribou, and the caribou can be the chief food for the wolves. Even so, the evidence is strong that the quality of caribou range is of fundamental importance in determining the abundance and distribution of the caribou and that a great deal of the wolf predation is borne by handicapped animals, the unattended calves, the aged, the crippled.

The centering of wolf predation upon handicapped individuals and parts of populations seems to be, if anything, still more pronounced when the prey is of the larger sizes of native hoofed animals, such as wapiti, moose, bison, and musk ox. Again and again, eyewitness accounts in the literature describe attacks of wolves upon ailing stragglers from the bison herds, opportunistic predation upon animals floundering in deep snow or upon unprotected calves, and so on. At least the moose, the bison, and the musk ox can be downright dangerous for wolves to attack unless the wolves do find them at a disadvantage.

PREDATION UPON SONG BIRDS has long worried bird protectors. Cats, screech owls, bird-hunting hawks, and bull snakes have all been noted to prey upon this or that small bird in lawn shrubbery, gardens, golf courses, or farm wood lots or pastures. We may properly ask just what difference does it make. We can still have plenty of song birds of the species that are most heavily preyed upon.

The song birds include species on which many great studies of that form of social intolerance known as territoriality have been made. They include species that display some of the most stereotyped behavior in restricting rights of individuals to certain areas. When territorial claims are made and fought over and settled, the distinctions between "mine and thine" go far toward determining how many birds of a given species can really live or be accommodated at a given place. Of course, when territorial behavior weakens or breaks down, as after the breeding season, the birds may flock or move about with so much freedom from interference by their own kind that it is hard to say what parts of populations may then be labeled "surplus" and what may not.

Mary M. Erickson's[51] study of wren-tit populations on a 16.7-acre area at Berkeley, California, is informative. She found, in this highly territorial species, that pairs renested several times if necessary to hatch their one brood each breeding season and that the territorial habit tended to keep the population constant. Her data for the two full years for which she had records show an increase from forty-five adult birds (including five unmated) in March, 1932, to seventy-six, or a 69 per cent gain by the end of the breeding season, compared with an increase from thirty-nine birds (again including five unmated) in March, 1933, to seventy-five, or a 92 per cent gain.

With respect to song birds that bring off more than one brood in a season, the evidence on automatic adjustments or compensations may be more noncommittal. Renesting in response to losses of egg clutches is of common occurrence, and loss rates tend to be higher and productivity lower as breeding densities increase; but rates of gain in relation to spring populations do not invariably conform to anything recognizable as definite patterns.

In part, this lack of conformity may mean that not enough accurate figures have been obtained to bring out the conformities that do exist, for it is hard to calculate net productivity when the young of each brood disperse from the study areas soon after they are fledged. On the other hand, I have more than a little suspicion that when a conformity does not show up, it may be for the chief reason that it does not exist. The glimmerings of evidence that mixed populations of song birds (considered collectively) may better conform to definite patterns than may populations of some particular species of bird (considered alone) suggest an explanation for some of the variations that are so troublesome analytically.

In this connection, I think of how many times I have noted the distribution of nesting populations of redwinged and yellowheaded blackbirds on Iowa marshes. Reed or cattail or bulrush clumps in the center are patently the choicest habitats for the yellowheads, and the marsh-margin growths of bulrushes are the habitat that the redwings seem to choose for their very own. This does not mean that redwings never occur in the central reeds nor yellowheads in the rushy shore zones, but each species shows what certainly look to be habitat preferences. Within their preferred habitats, either the redwings or yellowheads may be presumed to nest and rear their young with as much security from predatory enemies as could be expected.

Between the favored rushy fringes of the redwings and the reed and cattail clumps of the yellowheads may be patches and belts and even wide expanses of marsh growths, a sort of overflow zone, that neither redwings nor yellowheads rate as choice but in which either or both species may live. Between shore and the deep-water reed and cattail clumps, I have seen extensive areas of river bulrushes dominated by redwings one year, by yellowheads the next, and with mixed nesting populations conspicuously in evidence. A big question is: What in the way of handicaps may each blackbird species impose upon the other in such tracts, since the tracts apparently represent the less choice habitat for both the redwings and the yellowheads?

I have never discovered a plausible reason why redwings and not yellowheads, or *vice versa*, should be here or there among these in-between stands of river bulrushes.

It is the type of situation in which each species might have a depressive influence on the other after the combined population of blackbirds reached certain population levels. I think of something similar to the responses of mixed populations of gallinaceous birds. If one species happened to thrive, it might be in large measure at the expense of the other.

We could make some real progress on questions of population effects of predation and competition if we learned more about what constitutes the different grades of habitat for a song bird species. From Gunnar Svärdson's[52] account of habitat selection by Swedish wood warblers, one may conclude that warblers arriving at their breeding grounds know exactly what they are looking for in a way that, like habitat selection of McCabe and Blanchard's deer mice, eludes human perception. Whether or not human observers can detect the differences in detail or lay of land, or whatever it is that makes a livable niche for one species and not for another, quite certainly the distinctions between niches may be fine and still mean much in determining what species may be especially vulnerable to predation at given times and places.

THE LITERATURE ON FISH populations of fertile inland waters of warm or temperate regions leads into more questions about niches, competition between species, and population effects of predation and other mortality. These waters show evidences of a rather definite carrying capacity which is expressible in weight of fishes rather than numbers of individuals per unit of area; and the carrying capacity often seems to have a definite value for populations of several species of fishes collectively rather than for single species considered alone.

When one species declines as another increases, and the balance swings back and forth between one species and another, we are entitled to suspect that such events have some connection with each other. D. H. Thompson[53] reported that the bass, crappies, bluegills, and other sunfishes of Lake Senachwine in the Illinois River valley totaled between fifty and fifty-five pounds per acre each year. In some years, there were ten times as many fish as in other years, but then the average weight was only one-tenth as great. In some years, the black crappie made up over 90 per cent of the total; in others, the black crappie was largely replaced by the white crappie and the bluegill. Predation (including cannibalism) among the fishes themselves was of this picture but it was not the whole picture. In addition, there were the many basic factors governing fish populations, the racial characteristics of physiology and behavior, and again the interplays of adjusting life and environmental niches.

Predation upon fishes by mammals and birds seems to me to differ somewhat from predation upon fishes by fishes or by other forms that actually live down there in the water. It is true that loons, grebes, cormorants, mergansers, and otters are such expert underwater swimmers that they also could be said to belong in the water, so maybe I am making too much of the distinction of their being air-breathers in my thoughts of them as fish predators. At any rate, they are not under the surface of the water among the fishes all of the time, in the sense that the bass and pike are.

Predation upon fishes by mammals and birds can be notable for its irregularities. It can be locally heavy, as when herons concentrate about the puddles of a drying bed of lake, marsh, or stream; or when large numbers of American mergansers winter along a stream where the trout are vulnerable. The fishes of a body of water may suffer nothing but the most incidental sort of predation from the minks frequenting the shores; or from the scattered herons standing in the shallows; or from a grebe or tern, a rare loon or osprey staying for only a few days. Or, another year, the fishes of that same body of water may feed a big flock of pelicans for several weeks.

High fecundity and compensating growth rates of fish populations of the richer waters certainly do much to modify population effects of the predation they draw, chiefly in decreasing numbers and increasing sizes of individuals as predator pressure increases. This is a most desirable tendency from the standpoint of fisheries management in waters where the biggest problems result from crowding and stunting of fish populations. Often, what a fish population may need more than anything else to put it in a state of healthy balance, and to improve its yield for fishermen, is sufficient attention from fish-eating animals to take a big cut out of the number of fishes already present.

Fishes of food-poor waters of mountain lakes or northern wilderness regions are slower growing and less resilient under predatory pressures. Big fishes get to be big in the more remote wilderness lakes in spite of slower growth rates, for the principal reason that they may live longer. However, there is resilience in these fish populations, too, and the splendid fishing that the white man found at the time of his first visits was itself proof of good adjustments between fish populations and their native predatory enemies.

ONE TYPE OF PREDATION that can be conspicuous and subject to varying interpretations is that which centers upon mass abundances of vulnerable prey animals. The gorging of predators upon the grasshoppers of late summer prairies is such a phenomenon and the variety of flesh-eaters or insect-eaters taking advantage of this food resource can hardly be enumerated. Yet, what does it mean biologically except that many eaters of grasshoppers eat and may be presumed to benefit to some extent from the eating?

The predation upon game fishes at fish hatcheries and game birds at game farms is so well known that a large segment of the public gets its ideas of predation from what happens under such artificialized conditions. Some of the most immoderate and sweeping "anti-vermin" campaigns affecting the American out-of-doors have been instigated by men familiar with the severity of predation losses on game farms, applying their special-case experience to over-all problems of game or wildlife management.

Let there be no doubt about it, a game breeder is often in a position to see extremes of predation. From small hawks to large hawks, the slow, the swift, the agile, the clumsy—everything from sparrow hawks to eagles (except the strict specialists such as the snail-eating Everglade kite)—may be expected to find some victims at a game farm. The owls, little and big, the crows, jays, grackles, shrikes, weasels, minks, skunks, raccoons, house cats, bobcats, opossums, dogs, rats, squirrels, the larger snakes, in fact anything that could prey upon creatures the size of large insects could prey upon pheasant chicks.

Not even the extreme types of predator-prey relationships found at game farms are without their evidences of compensatory trends, of life adjusting to patterns. W. B. Grange and W. L. McAtee[54] are qualified to come to conclusions on this subject. They found that, despite the diligence with which predators may be trapped and shot on the premises of American game breeders, the yearly toll taken by predators was almost constant on many game farms, anyway. Whether the predators were many or few, the vulnerability of the concentrated life on the game farms (or fish hatcheries or poultry establishments) still remained the basic cause of heavy predation losses.

Grange's experience has been both with conventional methods of rearing in pens and with practical wildlife management on the land. In practical wildlife management he has been outstandingly successful. The area of wild country in central Wisconsin that he managed for commercial game production encompassed about ten thousand acres, and he placed his emphasis in management upon regulation of plant succession to keep the habitat in the best possible condition for a rich and varied and essentially free-living wildlife. He achieved his gratifying and unusual abundance of game despite an almost total lack of repression of the predators that lived in what might be called normal abundance on his land.

One more special-case type of predation may be mentioned. The severest depredations of which I have read were those resulting from predatory species (especially members of the dog or weasel families) becoming introduced on islands having vulnerable prey populations. Arctic foxes reaching and preying upon nesting concentrations of sea birds, exotic rats or cats wiping out indigenous forms of life on temperate zone or tropical islands, racially new enemies finding unwary or unadaptable prey any place—all furnish examples of severe or almost unbearable predation. We need not expect to find evidences of compensations or automatic adjustments in island populations that became extinct a short time after some formidable introduced predator started exploiting them.

But extinction, even on a local scale, is not the inevitable result of the impacts of strange predators upon prey that is both vulnerable and restricted in distribution.

So we see almost everywhere we look evidence of the resilience of prey populations. Resilience can be more than high fecundity allowing for high losses; it can be a built-in tendency for populations to adjust to variations in natural factors, including predation. It does not follow that compensations in wild populations must compensate for everything, or that adjustments to any changes must be perfect, but most species that have lived on the earth for millions of years may be expected to possess a minimal ability to take care of themselves if living in places where they are adapted.

I do not visualize any all-comprehensive formula by which the role of predation in the population dynamics of animals may be expressed, but the view I have expressed many times in this book still seems logical to me: *that the more a prey population is basically limited by some non-predatory feature of its environment, or by its own intolerance of crowding, the less it can be basically limited by predation.* I do not say, and never have said, that predation cannot be a limiting factor with some populations; but, with the living forms with which I am most familiar, I believe that the population effect of predation is often greatly overrated, whether we use the expression "limiting factor," "controlling factor," "regulating factor," or some other term denoting comparable influence.

It is true that my specialties for study have all been more or less territorial forms, those displaying a high degree of intolerance toward concentrations of their own kinds past certain population levels. They have all shown rather sharp lines of demarcation between parts of populations that lived securely and parts that lived vulnerably in relation to predatory enemies. But the territorial forms, which include so many of our mammals and birds, are an important part of Life, and, if we learn more about how predation does or does not affect them, we surely learn something worth knowing.

PART THREE: IN SUMMING UP

12

THE PHENOMENON
OF PREDATION

"Nature's way is any way that works." My students know I like that expression. As a generalization relating to the opportunism and adjustments of Life, relating to the eaters and to the eaten, it has wide application.

Predators kill and eat the animals they know as prey, however they are able to do so. They prey according to their opportunities, their adaptations, and—sometimes— their psychological preferences. Their predation may be rather indiscriminate; that is, within common sense limitations. It may be highly specific, highly selective. It may grade into the related phenomenon that we refer to as parasitism. When the prey consists of eggs or sessile animals, it may not differ fundamentally in its operation from grazing by herbivores.

For that matter, certain peculiarly adapted plants may prey upon animals. Bladderworts capture and digest small crustaceans in their traplike organs. Pitcher plants and sundews take insect victims as a regular way of life. And, whether one thinks of bacteria or viruses as being predatory or parasitic or saprophytic, the basic natural laws to which they conform in their exploitation of the exploitable are still those applying to the phylogenetically higher organisms.

The common denominator throughout is exploitation of the exploitable; but, if we think of just that in considering the phenomenon of predation, we may easily oversimplify. For a lot of evolution has consisted of shaping the patterns of interrelationships of living things with each other and with their physical environments. Diversity and complexity in these interrelationships are wholly consistent with diversity and complexity in the forms of living things.

I do not advocate straining to distinguish between borderline cases of predation and parasitism nor trying to judge precisely where predation and parasitism leave off and exploitation of dead or dying organic material begins. Preoccupation with definitions in relationships that by their nature have much leeway in them can, I think, defeat understanding. Just where do we logically put the dividing line between what a feeding mosquito does in taking a meal of either blood or juices, what a spider does to a fly, a water bug to a minnow, a robber fly to a grasshopper, a sea lamprey to a lake trout or a whitefish; what a killer whale or a shark or a bird of prey or a wolf does in eating something, alive or dead; what a snapping turtle does when it feeds upon algae, scavenges upon anything dead, eats the tails off live fishes on a fisherman's stringer, or grabs a coot by a foot?

Gradations exist, whichever way we look, and I shall not further belabor what seems to me the pointlessness of labeling categories beyond what the facts justify. Regardless of the opportunism common to a bacterial infection and a violent attack by a genuine tooth-or-talon predator, the obvious differences are such as to merit separate treatment; and there is plenty about the phenomenon of predation that may be discussed in ordinary terms of animals being sought by or escaping from other forms that would kill or eat them, (or, of them) if they could.

RELATIVELY FEW MAMMALS and birds are adapted to exploit only a particular kind of prey. One of these is the Everglade kite, which has a hooked beak that is exactly right for extracting soft parts from the shell of a single genus of snail, and so the bird lives. The Canada lynx and the arctic fox may, on occasion, be all but restricted to only certain of the foods available to them, apparently because of their own lack of adaptiveness; on the other hand, their relatives, the bay lynx or bobcat and the red and gray foxes of central and southern North America, may readily eat a wide variety of foods. Gray wolves having opportunities to do so may, by choice, prey almost exclusively upon white-tailed deer. But predatory mammals and birds collectively are omnivorous feeders compared to the vast numbers of insects showing rigid selectivity in their predatory (or parasitic) behavior. Far down the phylogenetic scale are extremely host-specific viruses and bacteria, as well as some showing great versatility. The virus of rabies, the bacterium of tularemia, and the roundworm causing trichinosis each can attack an astonishing variety of at least warm-blooded host animals.

Food preferences or hunting techniques based upon individual learning are not restricted to higher vertebrates, though they naturally tend to be prominent among the more intelligent animals. Next to man, I would say that members of the dog family—individual red foxes, coyotes, gray wolves, domestic dogs—can show as much special choice of prey as any animals of which I know. The favoritisms and originality that some of these animals develop in their preying may at times result in unusually severe local exploitation of a vulnerable prey population. Even prey species that are living with notable security from other predators may at times suffer from concerted canine predation—I have known instances of this sort in my studies of predation by foxes and dogs upon muskrats and ground-nesting birds.

But, modern studies on predatory activity of lower vertebrates have demonstrated that learning can have a pronounced influence on their food habits. Fishes learn to take certain food items. Frogs may prey selectively through experience. Also, in recent years I have been gaining an impression from various sources that some insects and other active invertebrates may have capabilities for more individual preferences than we commonly have thought.

A morphologically advanced brain is evidently not an absolute prerequisite to a psychology of learning and choice.

LET US CONSIDER SOME of the ways that predation may be influenced by the psychology of either or both predators and their prospective prey—not forgetting that predators may generally take such prey as is easiest for them to get, suitable for their requirements, and recognized as food.

Some of the clearest examples of psychological influence in predator-prey relations are those in which adversaries do a good deal of testing out and appraising of each other's intentions and capabilities. The caution that predators show toward dangerous prey may be illustrated by wolves sizing up their prospects for attacking moose, bison, or musk oxen, or by the behavior of minks in the presence of formidable muskrats; but a predator's decision to attack or not attack may be quite unrelated to any threat of danger to himself. Wolves also appraise their chances with caribou that they have no reason to fear. Bird-hunting hawks may repeatedly test by preliminary feints the attitudes of small birds that could not possibly do more than escape.

Prospective prey that displays alertness toward predatory dangers yet conducts itself in a recognizably confident manner may discourage predators from attacking or cause the predators to desist soon after an attack is undertaken. I think we should give many predatory vertebrates credit for knowing pretty well when a serious attempt is not worth carrying out. Conversely, except for manifest injuries or helplessness, panic on the part of the prey may encourage attacks about as much as any other factor.

There may be, however, a still weightier psychological factor in some predator-prey relationships: social intolerance. One aspect of social intolerance—territoriality, or the defense of an area—has been best studied in mammals and birds, in some lower vertebrates, and in a relatively few invertebrates. Even among the mammals and birds for which it represents most nearly characteristic behavior, territoriality may exist in virtually all conceivable degrees of intensity, the year around or only part of a breeding season. It may represent either highly stereotyped or highly adaptive behavior.

A territory, as for a nesting pair of peregrine falcons, may be several miles across; or, as in some colony-nesting birds, approximately the distance that a bird can reach with its beak while sitting on its nest. For one species of East African bishop bird, a territory may have boundaries exceedingly resistant to change; yet, for a closely related species of bishop bird, a territory may be almost indefinitely compressible. There are examples of communal territories defended by whole colonies. There are examples of the defended territories of some waterfowl actually lying outside of the nesting grounds.

While usually directed against members of the same species, territorial exclusiveness may also take the form of antagonisms toward members of different species. Wrens and coots can be among the more savagely aggressive regarding territorial boundaries.

Savagely aggressive social intolerance is not necessarily restricted to defense of territories, as is illustrated by the mobbing of hawks and owls by crows and the mobbing of the crows, in their turn, by smaller birds. Social tolerances and intolerances may also be influenced by the traditions that either individuals or populations may build up. Much may depend upon what animals become accustomed to.

Concerning territorial and other intolerances, one may again easily regard Nature's way as being any way that works.

A wolf pack may lay claim to a whole watershed, and the wolves may jealously keep that area for themselves. Or, they may admit to their social order or their holdings neighboring groups of wolves or unattached individuals— depending upon interplays of wolfish (really doggish) formalities, necessities, and the tolerance or discrimination allowed by individual dispositions. The chief prey of these wolves in the northern Lake States and adjacent Canada are the white-tailed deer, which have social intolerances too weak to be much of a self-limiting factor; and

the deer may increase up to such numbers that they starve
and seriously damage their environment while so doing.
At least under some conditions, an adequate population of
wolves may hold the deer down to levels in better biological balance than populations not subject to effective
predation.

Social intolerances of minks may not fit too well into
the category of actually defended areas, but the intolerances do work to keep mink populations spread out. As
essentially solitary animals, their winter densities on the
marshes that are the most food-rich for them seem to level
off at between twelve and twenty minks per square mile. I
have never observed that any superabundance of readily

HAWK AND CROWS

available food ever resulted in concentrations of free-living minks to the extent that individuals would be likely to encounter each other with great frequency in their daily lives. It has always seemed to me that excess minks tend to withdraw from the mink-crowded places, though this might mean wandering or trying to live in ecologically inferior environment.

If North American minks have any one favorite food, I should say that it is the muskrat. Minks may at times subsist upon muskrat flesh almost as exclusively as wolves may upon venison—with the outstanding difference that the minks may not find the presence of large numbers of muskrats synonymous with availability of large numbers of muskrats as food. Our Iowa data show a peak fall population of about nine thousand muskrats living securely on a 935-acre marsh, despite the activities of about thirty muskrat-hungry minks. The distinction between availability to predators and mere presence of prey should be emphasized. In the case of our Iowa muskrats, the predation is centered upon overproduced young; upon the restless, the strangers, and those physically handicapped by injuries or weakness; upon animals evicted by droughts, floods, or social tensions; in general upon what is identifiable as the more biologically expendable parts of the populations.

I do not think that predation should be regarded as a true limiting factor of these muskrat populations. To the extent that predation operates only incidentally, removing little except the wastage parts of populations, it may make little difference to the population levels reached or maintained if the predation losses are light or heavy. I should say that the dominant limiting factor of a muskrat population is still its own sociology, within the frame of reference imposed by the material features of its environment.

Another predator-prey relationship in which severity of the predation suffered by the prey may be most misleading in offhand appraisals of population effects is that of the great horned owl and the bobwhite quail in north-central United States. Our year-after-year population case histories show heavy predation by low populations of owls

upon either high or low populations of quail, light predation by high population of owls upon either high or low
populations of quail, and much variation in between.
What counts in determining the populations reached or
maintained is not that the owls have quail to eat or that
the quail have owls to eat them. Both species are highly
territorial and show a strong degree of self-limitation independently of each other. Neither big owl nor small quail
permits itself under normal conditions to increase up to
levels that are biologically top-heavy. In this way each of
these two species has much in common, though one is
subject to very little predation and the other is subject to
a great deal.

In its workings, territoriality tends to separate the
haves from the have-nots in a population, with the holders
of "property rights" having tremendous psychological
advantages in whatever competition takes place. Proper
consideration of this factor calls for some modification of
conventional views as to the struggle for existence, the
ruthlessness of natural testings, and the nature of predation. The favored parts of a territorial population living
in relative social peace, well adjusted to their environmental resources may, in fact, have fairly easy lives. They
may not have to do much more than conduct themselves
according to their ordinary endowments to live securely
with respect to their ancient predatory enemies. In contrast, life can be anything but benign for the wastage parts
of a territorial population, and these are characteristically
vulnerable to predators.

Species having weak if any territoriality may show
much more violent fluctuations. It is quite understand-
able that the less a population is self-limited, the more it
must be limited by something else: predation, parasitism,
disease, emigration, malnutrition or exhaustion of food,
exposure to climatic emergencies, and the miscellaneous
troubles that become compounded whenever populations
get out of bounds.

SURELY, ONE OF THE principal differences to be seen in
predator-prey relationships of higher vertebrates and

invertebrates is linked with the relative importance of territoriality in these phylogenetically differing groups. Between the extremes represented by the most socially exclusive of the mammals and birds and, let us say, oysters growing on top of one another, many forms of living creatures have developed territorial behavior to some degree.

Lizards and fishes—among them chameleons, sunfish, and sticklebacks—include territory holders at least during their breeding season. Although territoriality in lizards and fishes may allow great numerical abundance, populations of these forms may still show distinct tendencies to level off with increased crowding and, often, with apparent independence of predatory ememies. Phylogenetically down-scale a little more, we also find insects and crustaceans capable of displaying effective antagonism toward possible competitors, and their populations may have at least some of the features of thresholds of security and vulnerable overflows. I have seen dragonflies perched on tops of cattail stalks patrolling their holdings, and, if this behavior is not truly territorial, it looks like the next thing to it.

J. H. Pepper[55] published in the mid-fifties a most informative comparison of the population dynamics of Montana grasshoppers and Iowa muskrats. As far apart in their taxonomic relationships and as diverse in their living requirements as grasshoppers and muskrats are, they may show social intolerances and habitat responsiveness that appear, broadly, not too dissimilar. Parts of grasshopper populations may, like the muskrats, be relatively well situated; other parts, crowded into inferior habitats or beset by the frictions of overpopulations, are more exposed to miscellaneous mortality factors, including predation.

I now believe that much of the predation suffered by grasshoppers—which I had long assumed to be more random, more of a gradual-attrition type—falls instead in more of an off-and-on, secure-and-insecure dichotomy.

(I am reminded that once I had even thought the predation borne by an abundant muskrat population was proportional to the numbers of muskrats and the predators preying upon them, whittling down the general musk-

rat population little by little. That was before any attempts were made to inquire more deeply into what was
happening. With careful local analyses, it became apparent that the predation that suggested gradual attrition was
not in fact working that way on the muskrat population
as a whole; it was conforming to the same overall rules of
order that the Iowa muskrat studies had brought out again
and again—parts of the population lived very vulnerably
while other parts retained their security.)

When re-examining questions of social intolerances
and population effects of predation in the animal kingdom, I am not surprised that few pat answers come to
mind.

Predator-prey relationships are just as likely to be
affected by social frictions, established property rights, and
complex behavior patterns even if the participants happen
to be classed as lizards, fishes, insects, and crustaceans
rather than as mammals and birds. Nor should the greater
collective fecundity of lower vertebrates, with corresponding individual cheapness of life, be considered a complete
explanation for the lesser territoriality of lower vertebrates. Even among higher vertebrates, the strongly territorial gray wolf with close family ties has, on paper, a far
higher biotic potential than its prey, the deer and caribou
that may congregate in tremendous numbers. Nor can
the lesser territoriality of lower vertebrates be wholly explained in terms of their lesser intelligence and lesser
adaptiveness, for territoriality reaches some of its most
pronounced evolutionary peaks in birds, which as a class
are less intelligent and adaptable than mammals.

The point is, once more, that Life selects for what
works, irrespective of our human efforts to define and
classify.

WE MAY NEXT CONSIDER something else that Life selects
for, something that is very often interlinked with or a by-
product of territoriality. It is the tendency to compensate,
one of the prime upsetters of both theoretical and "common sense" calculations as to how Nature's equations
work.

Intercompensatory trends in rates of population gains and losses go a long way toward conferring a singular degree of biological safety upon species that are subject to vicissitudes. In a resilient population, severe loss rates may in effect substitute for each other without mounting up excessively high in total. Extraordinary losses through one agency may automatically protect from losses through many other agencies. The death of one individual may mean little more than improving the chances for living of another one. Furthermore, in some species, extraordinary losses may be compensated by accelerated reproduction, more young being produced in consequence of more being destroyed.

From these considerations, it can be perceived why I am not inclined to accept mere conventional vital statistics as a suitable base for appraising the population effects of predation. More may be needed than figures as to how many individuals are brought into the world and how many or what proportions die through predacious agencies.

Whether the population resiliences permitted by the compensatory trends enable a species to escape being dangerously reduced by great trials, or to resist changes in *status quo*, or to fill up biological frontiers with explosive rapidity, they obviously can be an important part of Life. Whether the purposes of human manipulations of animal populations are to encourage or discourage a particular species, in connection with nature protection, fish and game management, or pest control, we cannot afford to forget the fact that natural compensations can nullify much of the effort that fails to take them into proper account.

The renesting prowess of some popular game birds is sufficient to confound many of the pencil-and-paper figurings of laymen, who easily become emotional at the thought of a crow or a skunk destroying a clutch of eggs. To the bobwhite quail and the ring-necked pheasant, the loss of a clutch or two early in the nesting season does not necessarily signify a corresponding net decrease in productivity of young. For species constituted to hatch only one clutch of eggs per year and those that have a long breeding season and several possible nesting trials with which to do it, half to three-quarters of their nests may fail and still allow the breeding females to fill their one-brood "quota" for the breeding season. The more resilient nesters among waterfowl seem to be almost as persistent and as ultimately successful in their renesting efforts. Within broad limits set by physiology and climate, it may not really matter whether the crows, skunks, raccoons, or other wild egg eaters plunder a large proportion of the nests or whether they do not. It may all come out much the same in the end.

Breeding resilience may also compensate for high juvenile mortality in some of the more prolific mammals. This, too, should not be confused with the mere production of immense numbers of young to allow for or to compensate in advance for heavy losses. Rather, the population adjusts to the social tolerances of the species and the status of the habitat. Extraordinary losses of young may *stimulate* reproduction. For the muskrats of north-central United States, averages approaching four litters during a breeding season may be born to uncrowded adult females living under favorable conditions. Averages as low as a litter to a litter and a half may satisfy crowded populations in the same kind of place. But, if the early born young suffer very high rates of mortality—as through the agencies of floods and epizootic disease on the north-central study areas—even crowded populations may give birth to many additional litters that plainly would not have come into existence had it not been for the severity of the earlier losses.

After the young of these resilient breeders are hatched or born, compensatory trends in loss rates go into a substitution phase. While a minimal loss of young during the rearing season is inevitable under the best of conditions, a lot of the postbreeding "shaking down" of overproduced young depends upon the extent to which their environment is already filled with their own species. The net population increases often tend to follow definite curves or to reach certain density levels, often in conformity to year-to-year mathematical patterns—patterns that look unaffected by changes in kinds and numbers of predatory enemies, the impacts of the less sweeping deadly emergencies, and so on. We can thus see evidence of balancing and counterbalancing that make meaningless any calculations as to population effect based solely upon the numbers or percentages of individuals that may die through this agency or that.

Muskrat populations comfortably situated in rich environment may give birth to many young and rear most of the young born; those populations that are beset by endless stress may give birth to few young and rear comparatively few of those. When the social squeeze is on and life is hard, there are bound to be heavy losses from various agencies, including predation from different kinds of predators. Still, I cannot see that such predation actually operates as a limiting factor—at any rate insofar as something else is doing the real limiting. Particularly do I find it difficult to see why the mink, for example, may be considered a muskrat-limiting factor simply on the basis of the large numbers of muskrats the mink as a species may kill. In the absence of minks the muskrats generally neither reach nor maintain their numbers at perceptibly higher density levels than they do in the presence of the minks. The Iowa case histories of mink-muskrat relationships repeatedly support this view.

We may see similar evidences of social interplays and compensations in the extensive literature on population dynamics. Poison-depleted rat and ground squirrel populations have responded to lessened social tensions by accelerated rates of increase. The red fox, despite sport and bounty hunting in north-central United States, not only maintains its numbers at high levels in suitable range but also, I should say, thrives in spite of heavy hunting mortality. Heavily hunted deer populations produce greater numbers of twin fawns than the less hunted. Mallard ducks, though overshot by man, have remarkably low "natural" loss rates compared to blue-winged teal, subject to relatively little human hunting. Heavily exploited stocks of sport or food fishes have faster growing individuals than less exploited stocks in the same waters. One Iowa lake of which I know that most consistently produces the greatest numbers of large bullheads is at the same time among the most heavily fished.

Of course, one could easily overgeneralize. I am aware that many species of birds do practically no renesting. Some grouse may normally make but a feeble attempt at renesting and then only if their initial clutches of eggs for the season are destroyed before the laying birds have invested much time in incubation. The shortness of the summer does not leave arctic-nesting waterfowl much time for renesting, at best, if the late-hatched young are to develop enough to fly out before freeze-up. Even the bobwhite quail may lose its renesting resilience under the influence of severe and prolonged drought. There are conditions under which the most resilient of species will not try to breed at all, under which there seems to be no chance for any kind of compensatory balancing, at any stage of life.

As concerns either the lack or the prevalence of intercompensatory trends in the population dynamics of invertebrates, a great deal remains inconclusive. Many leading students of the population dynamics of insects regard compensatory tendencies as of general application throughout the animal kingdom; another very respected entomologist regards compensatory predation as probably uncommon in insects.

Perhaps it may be argued that, concerning phenomena in which almost anything can happen, everyone can make whatever choice pleases him, but I do not think that that is a scientifically fair judgment to make. In studies of the exploiters and the exploited, we deal with adaptations of long standing. We need not restrict ourselves to the animal kingdom to see this. Grass grows anew in response to grazing, and part of the annual production of a pasture depends upon the grazing pressure that it receives.

THE LITERATURE ON BIOLOGICAL control has among its bewildering figures, variables, mathematical models, and claims and counterclaims some examples of cause and effect that look quite clear. Some of the evidence as to controlling or regulating influence of predation upon invertebrate prey populations can be duplicated by experimentation practically at will or verified by repeated observations of natural events that fall into patterns.

Granted that we must know what preys upon what, we should also know about relative severities of predation drawn by the prey, provided that we do not thereby conclude overmuch. I have nothing against the idea of exploring what can be explored with the aid of theoretical means, but I would hesitate to endorse anything following the line of thought that a given theory must be correct because it has no alternatives its proponents would rate as logical. I confess also to a distrust of conclusions derived from mathematical models that assume more randomness of contacts between predator and prey than I am accustomed to see under natural conditions—though, by this, I do not contend that randomness cannot or does not occur in true-to-life equations.

In general, the more patently the evidence comes from the land (or the water) itself, the more reassured I feel as to its validity as any sort of proof, one way or another. And, while even long-term experimentation on the land with predator-prey (or parasite-host) relationships very frequently gives rise to negative or inconclusive results, there are enough convincing cases of populations of especially insect prey responding either to increased or decreased predator (or parasite) pressure to demonstrate cause and effect. Some of the examples coming out of biological control experiments are by now classics in the literature on predation. I suppose that almost everyone who has done much reading in biology knows about ladybird larvae preying upon plant lice. Similar examples that are scarcely less celebrated have been reported from many regions of the world. Indeed, the books and review papers on biological control attest to a tremendous amount of collective experience with this sort of thing and to the frequency with which, among the invertebrates, a predator can influence the population levels of its prey; and the idea of managing entomophagous insects through environmental manipulation, establishment of "refuge stations" in intensively cultivated areas, etc., is not new in applied entomology. I am uncertain, however, as to how effectively this type of management may increase an economically desirable type of predation.

The role of insectivorous birds in pest control has been threshed over for decades, sometimes with extravagant claims and assumptions. In my opinion, the desirability of having birds around can be well advocated on grounds other than the quantities of insects that they eat, without straining to justify them economically. When it comes to appraisal of bird predation upon insects, worms, slugs, and the small creatures we call "pests," the questions continue to arise as to whether such predation does have a controlling influence.

The few case histories of control of insect populations through bird predation that look convincing to me have one thing in common: superlative intensity of predation. A small garden enclosed by luxurious shade trees and shrubbery may concentrate the feeding of a large number of birds and thus have its insect populations reduced by the sheer weight of the predatory effort exerted. A homely analogy may be seen in neighborhood robin depredations on the cherry crop ripening on someone's lone backyard tree. But, in considering predation by birds upon invertebrates on a more spacious scale, it becomes more difficult to argue from sober facts. The property on which I live never seems to have any dearth of earthworms, however much the local robins may be observed pulling them out of the ground or collecting them in their bills after rains. (Neither do the ground-plowing moles seem to affect earthworm numbers appreciably, as a spadeful of soil turned in any place suitable for earthworms will reveal at almost any time.) We see the chickadees working the tree branches, the flickers and meadowlarks out in the fields, the swallows feeding in the air and we know that they are eating insects, perhaps of known kinds and in quantities that might be calculated. But, aside from that, what do we really know about it?

Considering predation by birds on a still more spacious scale, I am willing to concede that the early Mormon settlers of Utah may have had good cause to erect a monument to cricket-eating gulls. The gulls, flocking to feed on the hordes of crickets that threatened the Mormon crops, very possibly brought the crickets under sufficient control to save the crops; but, from what I have been able to learn about this event, it seems to have been a matter of rather local concentration of gulls in response to a concentrated food supply; and I would doubt that the gull predation resulted in any significant population control of the crickets over truly immense areas.

This naturally leads to philosophical questions as to how much some degree of predation here and there and now and then by this predator or that may contribute to the control of an invertebrate species when added to its other mortality factors; and I am reminded, too, about all of the confusion between facts of predation and effects of predation that exists in the literature on vertebrates and invertebrates alike. The population effects of predation by raptorial birds upon mice and upon songbirds may be equated with the numbers of prey killed; so may predation by the mice and the songbirds upon the insects that these may kill; so may predation (or parasitism) by insect species upon each other, by the hornets, the dragonflies, the powerful biters and stingers of lesser creatures that cannot escape; and yet I should say that the grounds for imputing population control may be flimsy indeed without consideration of possible intercompensatory adjustments.

To SUM UP CONCERNING predation as a phenomenon with special reference to its significance in population control: As may easily be judged, I regard the outstanding source of error in appraisals of predator-prey relationships as confusion of the *fact* of predation with *effect* of predation. Apart from a number of extreme or dramatic cases of predation depleting prey populations in ways that are self-evident, my inclinations are to look very critically upon figures presented by themselves as proof of population effect. They may constitute no proof at all, however imposing they may be when superficially regarded.

For intercompensation remains one of the big answers

of prey species—especially of the less fecund or the only moderately fecund—to predation losses as well as to many other losses. On the basis of my own experience as a student of predation, the best advice I have to offer anyone interested in exploring the subject on his own responsibility, or to those trying to obtain workable concepts of its mechanisms, is this: Watch out for the compensations in attempting to distinguish between what does or does not count. When compensations are important in population dynamics, they simply cannot be ignored in calculations as to regulation effects of mortality factors if the truth is to be reached.

GOLDEN EAGLE

13

PREDATION
AND LIFE'S WHOLENESS

IN MY DISCUSSION OF predation as a natural phenomenon, I wish to restrict my usage to exclude such political and social activities of civilized man as may be called predatory. What man may do in the way of frauds, seductions, or piracies has been, I am glad to say, largely outside of my province as a student of predation.

What I regard as true predation, in the sense of a phenomenon that has been a part of Life presumably about as long as Life has existed on earth, is as natural as anything could be. It is as natural for organisms to exploit flesh as non-flesh. The fact that animals having predacious habits and adaptations sooner or later appear in essentially all long established animal societies having something to prey upon illustrates the fundamental naturalness of predation.

Predation belongs in the equation of Life.

To people who do not regard predation as an intrinsically evil thing, the beauty and prowess of some predators go far toward making them creatures of special interest. My own interest in predators, however, is not simply because of their attributes as predatory forms. I have no wish whatever to see Old World predators transplanted to the New World nor New World predators transplanted to the Old World—even if the transplanted predators would be among the most beautiful and perfectly adapted creatures on earth—and economically valuable to boot. Many of the predators that interest me most are what might be called the ordinary ones—the foxes and minks, the ordinary hawks and owls, the shrews and frogs and snapping turtles, and other flesh-eaters that belong where they live.

This concept of belonging is probably the most important in conditioning my attitude toward predators and predation. The mink, as a native North American, belongs in our North American out-of-doors, as a part of natural animal societies; and my view is that, in most regions of this continent, it is entitled to maintain itself. But, as a now-thriving exotic in the Scandinavian peninsula and in Iceland, I do not regard the mink as belonging there at all as a free-living wild species among the native wildlife, and I would experience no regret at learning of its extirpation from those areas. In Scandinavia, the presence of the mink may be classed as a superfluity, a biological upset resulting from human activities, whereas, in its native North American range, its presence contributes to the completeness of an evolutionary picture having the sanction and dignity of millions of years.

I recognize that man has not left a great deal of Nature undisturbed in regions that he has dominated, and that modifications in plant and animal communities through human agencies are inevitable as long as dense human populations live on earth. I am not advocating that we allow predators to commit ruinous depredations on any of our economic resources that might be vulnerable to them. Nor do I imply that there cannot be more predators of some kinds than might be desirable from anyone's standpoint.

Nevertheless, such native wildlife as can be preserved in the right places and made to fit in with human domination of the earth may be of singular value to modern man if only in contributing wholesome variety. To some of us, the relative completeness of plant and animal associations to be found in the less disturbed parts of the out-of-doors is the most priceless feature of the outdoor values that we have. Outdoor values are not wholly those of the shootable game or the catchable fish and certainly not those of mere teeming abundances of deer or common song birds or some other often commonplace forms.

In my opinion, native predators belong in our natural outdoor scenes not so much because they have a postulated or demonstrated monetary value or utility in the so-called Balance of Nature as because they are, it seems to me, a manifestation of Life's wholeness. I feel that the predators can contribute balance to human perspective if we are disposed to let them.

I HAVE SOME MEMORIES of rather intimate experiences with free living predators. One of my earliest field notes relates to an encounter with a mink. The date (May 23, 1919) was the last day of high school. After school had closed, I went for a walk along a creek on the outskirts of Brookings, South Dakota. I did this to get out in the country, to enjoy the sunshine and greenery and the other pleasant aspects of the Dakota outdoors in spring, to relax without immediate responsibilities, to look at tracks on mud margins, and to do some target practice with a pistol.

A hole in the creek bank was recognizable as a mink den, its vicinity strewn with crayfish remains and mink droppings consisting of more crayfish remains. Just inside the den entrance was a live crayfish, which I picked up. As I held it in my hand, a mink came out of the den hole, seized the crayfish from my fingers, and whisked with it back into the hole. I straightened up with a sensation of skin-prickling and breathlessness. I stood back watching the hole for some minutes in hopes that the mink might reappear but it did not.

At about the same time I had what I considered another rather intimate experience with a predator, this one a lynx in northern Minnesota. I wrote up a preliminary account sufficiently soon afterward to get the facts on paper. Much later, the following short article, "Of a lynx and a white cedar swamp," was published in the

Conservation Volunteer for March-April, 1953, issued by the Minnesota Department of Conservation:

Shortly before freeze-up some third of a century ago, I made a late afternoon camp on Lower Red Lake, to the south of Minnesota's Big Bog country.

Between the hilltop on which I put up the cruiser tent and the sand ridge of the lake beach itself was a narrow strip of white cedar swamp. On the sand ridge the outermost cedars were ten to fifteen feet from the water's edge when the lake was quiet and these formed a practically solid wall of vegetation that one had to push through to enter. Inside, on a necessarily limited scale, was the kind of swamp that once could be seen in and about the Big Bog, without saw and ax marks, without deer lines, without cigarette packages, cans, bottles, and Sunday supplements. Inside, punky old down logs lay more or less hidden by peat moss, peaty ridges marked the sites of still older down logs, dead and living cedars and balsams stood or leaned partly up-rooted from their own weight, and tangles of trunks and boughs and roots were draped with mossy and lichen growths. It all looked and smelled of age and agelessness, with trunks of living cedars two feet thick or larger and seed-lings and saplings growing where they could.

Like most wilderness niches of its type, this swamp did not have a great deal of animal life in plain view. There were the tame ruffed grouse in the aspens on the hill, the tame red squirrels and chipmunks and Canada jays. It was also a place for skunks and weasels and shrews and wood mice and snowshoe hares. A game trail had its deer tracks and the tracks either of wolves or of Indian dogs, or of both. But, to me, in retrospect, the real spirit, the *numenon,* of that swamp was the lynx.

I was scouring the frying pan with lakeside sand in the dusk when I heard the first squall of the lynx, perhaps a hundred yards away, then more of them, always coming closer, until they were coming from in front of me but still from inside the wall of sand ridge cedars. The squall-ing in front of me continued, enough above the ground level so that I visualized the animal standing with its forefeet on the sand ridge and watching through the hanging cedar boughs.

I stood at the edge of the lake, a flashlight in my hand. After possibly ten minutes of this, I decided to cross the swamp to the camp before the batteries burned out—so ahead I went, straight toward the lynx, putting on my best no-nonsense boldness.

Although the lynx became silent as soon as I headed for the sand ridge cedars, I was sure that it stayed around nearby. Twice, I had glimpses of what I thought was a square face amid the lit-up shadows and streamers and trunks, but, now in my mature years, I would not argue whether I saw the face or imagined that I did. The lynx may have lost a lot of brashness about the time that flashlight came toward it.

I climbed the hill to the tent and went to bed. Finally, one more cry, from away off along the lake shore. . . .

In the morning, I found that I no longer had the problem of trying to use up a slab of bacon that was too wormy to be appetizing yet too expensive to be thrown away. In the excitement of the evening, I had forgotten it beside the wet-down fire. Of course, an Indian dog could have taken it, but now I like to think that it may have been my lynx.

But, whatever really happened to the bacon, I like to think of a lynx living in the kind of setting in which a lynx belongs, of a piece of northern wilderness as it once was. I like to think of big-cat curiosity, of a wilderness creature being itself.

The winter that I spent in the Big Bog country, back in 1920–21, was one during which I had certain memorable relations with timber wolves. I cannot say that my relations with these wolves was intimate. I never got any in the course of my hunting and trapping—though, as a professional hunter and trapper, I could have used the money they would have brought me, and I certainly tried hard for them. Now, I feel that the memories I have of them are worth far more to me than any fur or bounty money that I could ever have gotten from their bodies.

I never even saw any of those wolves.

Although large tracts of this country had been cut over, burned over, ditched, mistakenly opened to agricultural settlement, abandoned by bankrupt settlers, and subjected at one time or another to about all of the misuse that man could inflict upon it with any chance of profit, the Big Bog still retained some of its special values as a wilderness and, to me, the wolves were a most important part of it. There, in the solitudes of perhaps a million sparsely populated acres were the wolves bounding along trails in deep snow, "hanging" about deer yards, howling in the cold moonlight.

The Big Bog had other wildlife—the deer and moose and even a remnant of woodland caribou in the right places, the bears and skunks and beavers and muskrats also in the right places, a few lynxes and fishers and otters, the foxes and red squirrels and snowshoe hares, deer mice, ruffed grouse, chickadees, Canada jays, weasels, horned owls—but nothing dominated my interest more that fall and winter in the Big Bog than those wolves that I never saw.

Another predator that I particularly think of in connection with the Big Bog as I knew it years ago is the great gray owl. This area is the only one in which I have ever seen the species living in the wild. With its big head and its long body encased in a fluffiness of feathers, a great gray owl off among the trees can appear even spookier than a barred owl. An almost ethereal frailty in relation to its outline size is further suggested by the small sizes of the prey it usually takes—mostly small mammals such as mice and shrews.

I find it easy to picture many other owls in other places: a tiny tame saw-whet, which appears now and then in Iowa during the winter months, staring from the midst of a clump of junipers, from a smilac tangle, or from a river-bank thicket of scrub willows; or a common screech owl living in the same sort of place. Or there may be a wintering flock of shortears or longears in a willow thicket or a clump of conifers, sitting, flying off or circling around an intruder; and their roosts have whitewash and pellets and bits of mouse or shrew fur and the scattered feathers of an occasional small bird.

"Sign" may show that horned owls are about: a yellow down feather sticking to a gooseberry bush, a couple of big bird tracks in the snow, a roosting site under a vine tangle or in some oak tree that retains its dry leaves throughout the winter. Perhaps, the hooting in dusk or darkness may be all that reminds one of horned owls. Perhaps, an owl may be the focal point of a flock of milling, cawing, mobbing crows. Or a snowy owl from the Canadian tundras may sit on fence posts and hay stacks or out on the ice about an open water hole in a lake, preying on the crippled or lead-poisoned ducks frequenting the last bit of open water.

I think of burrowing owls especially as the frequenters of the prairie dog towns I once knew in South Dakota. The owls might sit beside holes and at my approach run into their holes, whole families, with a ridiculous combination of dignity and expedience. I further think of prairie dog towns as the environmental niche of the black-footed ferret, despite the fact that I never actually saw a ferret (or any recognized "sign" thereof) at any dog town. According to the best evidence from the literature, this species of weasel was not abundant even when the white man came, and it since has become so rare as to seem near extinction. To me, the dog towns have always held a special interest because of the possibility that they might harbor ferrets.

When thinking of western North America, I naturally picture coyotes. I have so many memories of coyotes that I find it hard to pick out any special favorites. Those memories that recur to me most frequently may be simply of coyotes hunting ground squirrels or running off across a sagebrush flat or "singing" at night, or merely of trails in snow or mud or dust. I remember a dead heifer in a foothills pasture, to which I made daily visits to see how the coyotes managed to eat of the fresher meat as decay advanced. Many of my coyote memories are of how the animals succeeded in eluding me and my trap sets when I was a young fur trapper in western South Dakota. Most of all, my coyote memories are of the eerie yet beautiful howling I heard so often while camped in badlands or river "breaks" or lava flows or any place where coyotes lived. During the dusk and nighttime hours, the howling might be an accompaniment to my cooking supper or going to sleep—in a bedroll under the open sky or in a cruiser tent or in a cabin bunk. Or, I might awaken in the middle of the night to listen to a chorus. Almost always, I picture the coyote in a specific setting, and this doubtless contributes to keeping the memories vivid.

My memories of red foxes are much more than those derived from my years of work on their food habits. I have often gone out of my way to approach a consistently used fox retreat only in the hope of seeing the fox or perhaps of hearing one yap at me. I have sneaked up on sleeping foxes, followed fox trails, uncovered food caches, and snooped about den sites long after I had any special professional incentive for so doing.

Occasionally, foxes have given me much more than I expected in the way of memories but I think my wife had the most memorable experience of all. One day, waiting on a sandy shore while I waded out in a marsh, she watched the pups from a fox den frolicking about fifty feet in front of her. For several minutes they scrambled and tumbled and wrestled. They leapt over each other, their soft little fur jackets shining in the sunlight. Then, sounds I made out in the marsh warned them, and they poured back into their den hole before I knew they were there. All I saw was one of the adults running away from the den, along the shore and across a pasture.

Scania, in southern Sweden, is the place where I have felt that wild red foxes were most needed to counterbalance what was, according to my tastes, too orderly human land use. During the one winter I lived there, the foxes, though severely hunted, took care of themselves quite well. The opportunities I had to watch or "read sign" of hunting foxes afforded me some intimate views of the old contest between hunters and hunted. And even though an opportunity to peek out of the edge of a Scanian forest and watch a fox hunting was not in the category of specialness that I would assign to an opportunity to watch a wolf hunting on an arctic tundra, I was glad to settle for foxes in highly agricultural Scania. A fox hunting in slough grass or over a snowy meadow, sniffing, listening, pouncing, demonstrated in its own very special way what aliveness and alertness could be.

The badger of American plains and prairies has a squat, powerful build and digging prowess by which it may practically sink into the ground. I think the hardihood it can display in plundering nests of bees or hornets further makes it a distinctive animal. It may be seen asleep in the sunshine at the entrance of a hole, or young badgers may play outside of den openings. It is not necessarily man-shy, and I have seen a family of badgers sunning beside a den opening across the road from a central Iowa farmhouse.

I have a special badger memory from my youth on the home farm in eastern South Dakota. While cultivating corn, I saw a couple of half-grown young outside a den on a gravelly knoll. I left the horses and walked over to look. As I stooped over the den hole, the mother came up from behind and rushed between my legs on her way into the den. I saw her just before she reached me and thought I was being attacked, but the incident was all over before I could move.

That renowned champion minder-of-own-business, the striped skunk, has left me with a lot of memories— mostly very simple but pleasant. They are of mother skunks and trailing litters of partly grown black and white replicas walking along lake shores or hunting grasshoppers or grubs in pastures or stubble fields. They are of skunks in daylight or moonlight, of the tracks of a winter wanderer in wet snow, of frost filling the outer opening of a hibernation den, and of droppings showing bright colors of grasshoppers and crickets and beetles. During my later years, living in a relatively "skunkless" central Iowa, I have known excitement at discovering a used skunk den, with enough of a subdued aroma to remind me of the dens I found years ago in the hills and bottomlands of South Dakota. To me the odor of skunk is pleasant and its associations are pleasurable.

I think of striped skunks in the wildest Canadian North and along the lake shore ice-ridges of central Manitoba or Saskatchewan, in the foothills and high plains of northwestern United States, in the sand hills of Nebraska and South Dakota, in the Missouri Ozarks, on midwest farmsteads, in town dumps, and about stockyards.

I think of skunks partly redeeming, by their presence, the ugliness that is so often a by-product of human activity. Many times I have found the skunks of an abandoned set of farm buildings imparting their own positive values to what were otherwise the sorriest of eyesores. There, in dry weeds surrounding the old shells of house and barn and sheds and the heaps of rusted out and broken down farm machinery and junked automobiles, would be skunk trails. There would be used passageways under the foundation of the barn or leading into the open vegetable cellar or through the broken board fences. Heaps of plaster and glass and tar paper and rags and the accumulated dust of years would have skunk tracks and droppings. The scratched-out dirt under a well platform or porch would tell of skunks, and so would the settled butts of hay and straw stacks and the agricultural remnants in granary and mangers.

My residence in Iowa has given me many opportunities to observe an animal that occurred only sparingly in South Dakota during my youth—the raccoon. Mostly, the raccoons I have seen were only moving about in the riverside brush or along mud bar or lake shore, doing nothing that could be called especially remarkable. I might find one asleep in the opened top of a muskrat lodge. On a mild winter day I found two of them asleep in the dugout chamber of one lodge, their backs in sight from above. I have sat beside a pool in a drying stream bed in midsummer and watched a raccoon walk on the bottom with not much more than its head and back out of the water. It felt for crayfishes under rocks and in holes in the bank. Emerging from one pool—and looking as much like a drenched monkey as a raccoon—it walked across the dry pebbles and mud to the next pool, then went in once more, gravely and systematically feeling around for its prey.

I watched an otter hunting for the same kind of prey but not doing it in quite the same way. This particular otter was a tame one raised by Emil Liers, who was giving it exercise and a chance to supplement its diet with natural foods. I stood right over it, noting exactly what it did. It would dive and reappear with a crayfish or minnow or water beetle, swim on the surface, or feel under the rocks of riffles, grabbing here, grabbing there, as it rapidly worked the stream. That one experience did a great deal to fill in the details of "sign" I had earlier read from tracks, trails, droppings, and miscellaneous prey remains of otters in northern Minnesota, Wisconsin, and northern Europe.

The best place for otters that I ever found was in the same man-dominated Scania where I watched foxes hunt. Probably the most prized of my memory-trophies from the Scanian outdoors came from finding a large otter under the root tangle of a lakeside tree and from watching that wonderfully adapted and beautiful animal come out. A yard or more of rich dark suppleness poured from the opening, ran with easy bounds, swam through the crumbly ice at the water's edge and then disappeared in the reedy cover. There were the interesting land holes in which otters hid, scratching and scent stations by which they advertised their presence and marked their territorial property rights. There were trails of a couple of young animals running together on the beach sand and out across a frozen bay, one following the other in every little crook and loop and angle. There were tunnels in snowdrifts, prey leavings at the mouths of tile flows, muddy, bloody, icy landings, and wet retreats under stream banks.

It is of course through the tracks and leavings of prey and other material that those of us who watch for "sign" are most likely to become aware of predators in everyday life. We may, it is true, hear the redtails screaming, or see them circling over field or forest. We may see sparrow hawks hovering, or the winter's roughlegs beating wings and hovering like greatly overgrown sparrow hawks might hover. We certainly may hear the horned and barred and screech owls at night and see them from time to time, but even the more vocal owls often become more real through their "sign." The minks and weasels, the foxes and rac-

coons, the winter-active skunks and badgers, and almost
everything predatory that leaves tracks, are far more likely
to impress their presence and activities upon us indirectly
than through the few glimpses we may ordinarily obtain
of the animals themselves.

BECAUSE OF THE NATURE of predation, with predators
killing prey in order to live, the prey must typically be
more abundant than the predator population that it sup-
ports. Biologists have an expression for this idea: the
"pyramid of numbers." Teeming forms of exploitable
Life are at the bottom, the food base supporting vast numbers of creatures that in turn support somewhat less numerous and more complex societies of animals. As the pyramid reaches upward, let us say from the mice on land and
the small fishes in the water, we find societies of the mammals and birds we commonly think of as predators. There
are many different food chains or pyramids of numbers,
and whether we put a horned owl or a grizzly bear or a
wolf or a cougar or some other formidable or dominant
predator at the top of the pyramid, the predatory vertebrates comprise a group of relative scarcity. John and
Frank Craighead[56] estimated the numbers of prospective
hawk and owl prey and numbers of hawks and owls on a
township of land in southern Michigan during two winters. For one winter, ninety-six hawks of six species and
sixty-three owls of four species had below them in the pyramid of numbers about 361,600 small to medium-sized
mammals and birds. For the other winter the corresponding figures were twenty-seven hawks of five species, thirty-
two owls of four species, and about 128,900 mammals and
birds within the size ranges of prey for hawks and owls.
In addition, the township of land had populations of up to
fifteen foxes, thirty-six weasels, and twelve minks. While
it should not be assumed that the prey animals were at all
uniformly available to predators, such figures as fourteen
to eighteen hundred prey animals per predator illustrate
the relative scarcity of predators in a wild community.
This relative scarcity of predators is undoubtedly one of

the main reasons why many outdoor people can become so much interested in them, and when a predator is genuinely rare it can become a creature of surpassingly great interest.

Rarities, too, are in a special category from the viewpoint of human moral or ethical responsibilities, though a species that is a rarity in one locality simply because it occurs outside of its regular range is nothing to arouse special concern. For every living creature, there are places where it does not belong and cannot be expected to belong.

When I think of rarities toward which civilized man could show more evidence of a biological conscience than he usually does, I think of both plant-eaters and flesh-eaters. Yet there is a difference. Perhaps, let us say, the California condor may deserve protection neither more nor less than may some particular species of shorebird, parrot, crane, swan, goose, duck, deer, wild sheep, eagle, turtle, lizard, ape, woodpecker, or something else that lives only in precarious balance as a form of Life. And let us acknowledge that civilized man should strive to safeguard whatever needs protection. Nevertheless, I think the problems of safeguarding predatory rarities in our out-of-doors are, in general, much greater than the problems of safeguarding plant-eating rarities.

I remember reading a news item that depressed me not only because of the event described but also because of the attitude revealed. It reported the killing of a wolverine in one of the western states. I got from the article an impression that something had been done which merited acclaim. A committee of the National Park Service estimated, as of the late thirties and early forties, a total of about fifty wolverines for National Parks and National Forests in western United States. Still, I know there are people who would be willing to have our remnant of wolverines blotted out for the postulated benefit of those animals upon which wolverines might prey—the deer (of which we have millions) and the rabbits and grouse and other common animals (of which we have millions and millions).

From where I live, I would not have to go quite as far as the mountain chains of the Rockies to find other examples of human willingness—indeed eagerness—to destroy magnificent rarities to protect the commonplace. Even where timber wolves are living in places where they would be most unlikely to do any economic damage, and where man's only charge against them is that they kill deer that are already present in numbers past the capacity of the land to support, the general public seems yet to consider it a duty to rid the wilderness of its remnant of wolves. In the northern Lake States, where there are thousands of deer for every timber wolf that could prey upon them, wolves have a rarity value that should give them infinitely more interest as individual animals than the deer could have, however graceful and beautiful the deer may be.

Some people may ask what good is a rare species, predacious or not, if it is so rare that no one can expect to see it? Why bother about trying to protect it? Why not let it become extinct? Or we may have the cynical reasoning that if a species is of special interest and value because of its rarity, why not make it rarer still and thus increase still more its interest and value? My usual reply is that I feel it is reprehensible for us, as civilized beings, to act wantonly and arrogantly and, by so doing, to obliterate or take unnecessary chances of obliterating a living form.

I know that there are practical limits to what even the conservation-minded can do, and that we cannot expect to save everything from extinction, no matter how hard we may try. Geologically and phylogenetically speaking, extinction is racially as much a part of the process of living as is the death of individuals. It terminated the courses of countless populations of animals long before anything identifiable as man was on earth, and living things would still be experiencing racial decline and racial death if man were not so prominently on the scene. What I want to emphasize is that it would be fitting for civilized man to be less ruthless than he usually is in his treatment of non-human Life.

FOR MANY YEARS, I HAVE been especially interested in following the growth of an enlightened and rational attitude toward predators in the Scandinavian countries.

I am most familiar with the Swedish literature on conservation and have been impressed over and over again by how much sympathetic and constructive treatment rare predators receive in *Svensk Jakt*, the magazine of the principal hunters' organization. One issue has a drawing of a bird-eating gyrfalcon with text to the effect that perhaps twenty pairs live in the mountainous region of northern Sweden and that the hunters' organization has petitioned the royal government to give the species total protection over the whole country.

In 1956–57, of thirty-nine species of mammals and birds totally protected by Swedish law, fourteen were predatory species, including two eagles, the eagle owl, osprey, and arctic fox. Some other predators, such as the marten and the bear, which did not have total protection over the whole country, were nevertheless totally protected in many places. There are also substantial and seemingly increasing efforts in Sweden to have year round protection extended at least to the lynx, the wolverine, and to more birds of prey.

Efforts to protect rare predators are surely facilitated by Swedish public agencies compensating for damages these species may do to private property, but I think that another aspect of public relations may be still more effective: The philosophy expressed in popular writings regarding predation by rare predators upon game animals reflects a high esthetic level for an influential segment of the Swedish public. It is most reassuring to read discussions centering about the thesis that, although the eagle owl, the larger falcons, the lynx, and such, may kill much game individually, they themselves are worth far more as a part of living Nature than the game their present limited numbers could destroy.

I feel much the same way concerning not only the rarer but also many of the more common predators, and I am sure that I would even if I were unaware of the strictly biological aspects of predator-prey relationships and the mounting evidence that a large proportion of the predation borne by wild prey has less depressive influence on the prey than is popularly supposed. It seems right to me that horned owls should live in the woods where I hunt rabbits and that they should be entitled to hunt rabbits, too. Even if I might have somewhat more rabbits to shoot if I eliminated the owls, I still would not want to pay that price for more rabbits—or more pheasants or more of any other kind of shootable game for which the owls might possibly be competing.

As I look back on my own attitudes, I do not recall having had to outgrow any strong "crusader's complex" against predators. When young, I shot some cats and a few birds of prey because they were labeled "destructive" by conservation authorities. But, while I did not like to have minks preying upon the muskrats that I wanted for myself, I still intentionally left female minks as breeding stock on my traplines. My spoken justification for doing this was that the minks themselves were valuable fur bearers. In my own mind, I knew that this was not the whole reason nor even the real reason. I liked too much to have minks around as an interesting part of the out-of-doors to try to get rid of them.

This admission to myself that I wanted minks around because I wanted them had its counterpart in my wanting wild ducks and geese around the home farm, at times when they were responsible for crop damage as well as when they were not. It represented, moreover, a stage in the development of a form of intellectual honesty that afforded me increasing peace of mind as I grew older. Many more years were to pass before I would be psychologically ready to defend my love of the natural out-of-doors for what it was, without recourse to economic justifications that did not always justify. As the time came in my later years when I could frankly enjoy the sight or thought of a native predator rather irrespective—within wide limits—of what it ate, I knew that the capacity for doing so had long been there, though often partly obscured by the confusions of immaturity.

DESPITE THE GREAT FASCINATION that predation and predators hold for me, it is quite true that I can conceive of some predators as being too abundant. In our north-central region, red foxes and raccoons have probably been too abundant in most localities for more than a decade. On my central Iowa areas, when the foxes and raccoons reached abundances that seemed to be out of balance with other wildlife, as well as too great for their own good, I found myself thinking of them in somewhat the category of the overabundant plant-eaters—the overabundant deer, rabbits, muskrats, etc., that I have also seen in my life. However, recognition that foxes or raccoons could be too abundant, with no denial that they could stand reduction, implies no agreement with the "let's-get-rid-of-them-once-and-for-all" extremism that can manifest itself in so many places.

The Swedes, too, have been aware of having too many red foxes. Their foxes began their recent great increase about the time that ours did. The Swedes do a lot of fox hunting, advocating fox hunting both as a game conservation measure and as a sport. Nevertheless, I recall little rancor about foxes in the *Svensk Jakt* articles that I have read. Sweden, as well as the United States, has its anti-fox extremists, but the reasonable tone of the *Svensk Jakt* articles of the mid-fifties has been in pleasant contrast to some of the immoderate assertions appearing in our own American periodicals. The red fox is "Mickel" (a pet name) to the Swedes, and is depicted as neither a demon of slaughter nor as a creature possessed of unnatural restraint in its hunting.

Just to see what I would find, I looked through four volumes of *Svensk Jakt* and counted twenty-six articles dealing primarily with foxes, of which sixteen were about hunting or trapping foxes and eight were on natural history. In addition, there were two very clever (presumably fictitious) stories about foxes. Of seventy-four photographs or drawings of foxes (not counting advertisements), four were phantasy cartoons about foxes and poultry, six were of fox hunting by man, nine were of bagged foxes or of fox pelts, and fifty were of foxes hunting, snooping, watching,

resting, biting fleas, carrying game, quarreling, or otherwise behaving as foxes behave. One picture—a magazine
cover—was particularly charming; it was a photograph of a
fox in a patch of wildflowers. In none of the articles or
pictures could I see that any truths had been suppressed or
slanted to "prove" anything unrealistic.

In matters of beautiful and splendidly adapted and
interesting predators living where they belong, I do not
see that anything more than realism should ever be required as justification for their acceptance as a proper part
of Life in the estimation of civilized and perceptive man.

IT IS QUITE TO BE expected that predators and predation should elicit wide differences in opinion, public
policy, and practices at what might be called the operational level.

Some martens were by far the chief attraction that
two extensive forestry plantations had for me in Scania,
though the most cultured owner of a neighboring estate
undoubtedly reflected his gamekeeper's views when re-
marking, "Fortunately, the marten is rare." The exotic
rabbits on which the martens largely subsisted were both
shootable game and a serious pest. In my opinion, without
any real sacrifice of the game value of the rabbits, the best
use to which the rest of the rabbit surplus could have been
put would have been to feed the martens. To me, if I had
been an estate owner, it would not have been so unthink-
able to have also shared some other game or local wildlife
with the martens, conceivably even some of the fairly
abundant pheasants.

Another Scanian estate owner did express in a magazine article just such a sentiment with respect to wintering
eagles. He welcomed a golden eagle to his land as an
honored guest, whether it preyed upon his game or not.
However, I am afraid that Scanians of his outdoor philosophy, while maybe not quite as rare as either the martens
or the eagles, are very much a minority group.

The truth is that I did see and hear of persecution of
predators in Scandinavia that appeared senseless to me.

On lands having their wildlife so greatly impoverished in some ways, the old-fashioned intolerances could be depressingly extreme. On one strictly managed estate, the gamekeeper felt disgraced after a hunting party found that a fox had escaped him on an area that was supposed to have been kept "vermin free." Another area had a polecat (the only one I was able to locate during my entire sojourn in Scania) that was allowed to live unmolested in a rabbit warren that was thriving, but the neighboring gamekeepers were said to have been critical about such heresy.

Such intolerant attitudes are not restricted to thickly settled regions nor to properties managed for game by gamekeepers. People living in northern hemisphere wildernesses may show if anything even greater animosity toward predatory creatures, especially toward the larger ones.

Even when proven damage from predators is compensated by public agencies, there may be uncertainties, extra trouble, and other worrisome aspects to predation losses or fears of losses (or personal fears of formidable predators themselves) that people who are close to the problems may understandably not like. (As much may also be said about problems arising from overly close contacts with some wild species that can be vexatious or even dangerous to man without being the least predatory.) Add to the hard aspects of living in country that is marginal for human existence the ancient superstitions and traditions of predators being hereditary enemies, and the reasons are clear why local people may be unenthusiastic about preserving predators for the sake of having them around. The mere fact that some backwoods and wilderness people do like bears, lynxes, and even wolves, and do regard them as a proper part of their surroundings, does not alter the other fact that an economically vulnerable public and predators with expensive appetites usually do not get along well together.

There need not be much of a damage problem at all to arouse deadly hatred on the part of the public toward the predators. Kai Curry-Lindahl[57] has referred to the golden eagle as being one of the flesh-eaters having access to the thousands of reindeer carcasses spread out here and there over Lapland in late winter and spring. Naturally, the golden eagles feed on this carrion; so do foxes and ravens and whatever else that can do so. The golden eagle, having a Swedish stock of about a hundred nesting pairs and legally protected the year around, is, despite the legal protection, subject to a conscienceless persecution in many, if not most, places where it lives and nests. The female eagles are shot on their nests, the eggs and young destroyed —and this hatred relates to a predatory form that is really much less hated than the wolves.

OF ALL OF THE NATIVE biological constituents of a northern wilderness scene, I should say that the wolves present the greatest test of human wisdom and good intentions. The problems of rational wolf management are so complex, so beset by prejudicial extremes, so confused by misconceptions and half truths and false moral judgments that, to a large part of the public, the only wolf problem is one of getting rid of and staying rid of the wolves. The latter, to my way of thinking, is an appalling oversimplification loaded with potentialities for great mistakes.

There is no doubt in my mind that the big wolves of our livestock-raising plains and prairies had to be eliminated. They had to go from all places where their predatory prowess and expensive appetites came too much in conflict with human interests. But, while the presence of large free-living wolves is incompatible with stock raising, wolf predation upon big game in wilderness regions can be desirable from all standpoints, including the welfare of the game. For, over vast tracts of North American wilderness, predation by wolves or other formidable predatory enemies may be exactly what the game needs, above all else, to help keep its numbers within a healthy state of balance with its environment. Relationships between wolves and big game—elk, deer, caribou, moose, mountain sheep, and others—vary with the locality, and I have no infallible rules of thumb to propose for appraising wolf predation upon any of these species. But it does happen that some of the best examples of big game being well adjusted to its natural range come from places in North America that continue to have the most nearly normal populations of wolves.

Penalties for overuse of game range can be drastic. Excessive browsing pressure by heavy populations of hoofed game may deplete the better game foods to the point of ruin, so much that the range may not recover for decades, even with complete protection from browsing. The occasional starvation by the thousands of such animals as deer in the northern Lake States may be a minor evil compared to the damage those deer may have inflicted on their range as they starved. Those staple winter foods of Alaskan caribou, the branching lichens or "reindeer moss," may require a human lifetime for replenishment if damaged severely enough.

It is important, from the standpoint of practical management alone, never to allow big game range to deteriorate unnecessarily, whether in the wilderness or out of it; and, to the extent that the wolves serve a useful purpose in preventing or limiting deterioration of some big game range, it seems to me only logical that this should be taken into account.

Recognition that wolves are only wild dogs, with the curiosity, playfulness, and doggish behavior of dogs could also lead to more rational wolf management in wilderness regions. "Wolfish nature" can be in actuality a far different thing from the images of monstrous savagery that the public finds so credible.

The wolves that I am familiar with in central and northern North America are almost never a danger to human life and to the best of my knowledge really never have been. Apart from the very special danger of rabid wolves in places where rabies is prevalent, and the extremely rare cases of healthy wolves offering a threat to human life, the hazards of wolves to man's person are fictitious. The writers of horror stories involving wolves still have a lucrative market, but wolves seem to have a singular respect for living human flesh even when unafraid.

To me, however, the chief justification for having

wolves in wilderness regions lies in their being part of the wilderness—a wonderfully interesting and thrilling and integral part. To me, absence of wolves in wilderness regions where they may reasonably be said to belong represents a fundamental lack that is all the more regrettable to the extent that it is needless or the result of human misconceptions or narrowness of outlook.

IT IS TRUE THAT THE gray wolves of our northern wilderness regions comprise a highly resilient species. When the wolves find the right living conditions, they may be able to withstand a severe human toll and rapidly fill up underpopulated parts of their remaining range, range that is underpopulated in terms of what the range can support and what the wolves themselves will tolerate socially.

The wartime and postwar dislocations of human populations in eastern Europe resulted in ecological and other changes that were very favorable for the wolves. The animals not only increased greatly in regions that had reverted to backwoods or wilderness but also overflowed into thickly settled lands to the west from which wolves had been absent for many decades. That this new population of rather uninhibited wolves made itself unpopular is indicated by the frequent use of the expression "wolf plague," or its equivalent, in European magazine or newspaper articles. While statements as to the "almost unbelievable" increase of wolves and the immensity of their depredations upon sheep and other livestock should be considered in the context that damage from free-running domestic dogs is regularly reported as wolf damage, plenty of evidence remained that the wolves made a tremendous comeback when they had such a good chance.

Not so long ago, I read an official report on wolf control in a North American wilderness area. Reference was made to a systematized "assembly line" type of control, to wolf control being a cold, hard, but very efficient business. Through the use of the overwhelmingly effective poison known as "Ten-eighty" in baits dropped from aircraft in places where the chances of animals other than wolves getting to it were slight, the campaign on two hundred thousand square miles resulted in a reduction of wolves incomparably more pronounced than anything that could have been achieved by more haphazard methods.

The report was carefully prepared, reasonable in its attitude, and, so far as it went, at least on paper, I have no objections to it. In fact, I should be inclined to settle for the type of responsible predator control it evidently represents. The author stated that his purpose was to point out facts and figures and not to discuss pros and cons of predator control. I concede his justification in thus limiting the scope of his discussion.

My greatest concern is not over what this campaign did in an area having a high wolf population—or even in parts having range overpopulated by big game—so much as with what it demonstrated in lethal potentialities. With efficiency still more refined, the "cold, hard business" could have chilling prospects, indeed, from the standpoint of retaining in existence some of the wilderness forms of wolves (or any form of Life) that the wrong person in administrative power might decide to obliterate.

Frankly, I do not like the idea of anyone or any faction having the power to say, "Go ahead," in response to an impatient, "Why not get rid of them once and for all and get it over with?"

But I know that I have to face it. In quarters where the sole interpretation of anything to be called a wolf problem is, categorically, getting rid of the wolves, modern man has the means for doing so. Modern man has power for almost any kind of rash use.

IT SEEMS TO ME almost a general characteristic of humankind to see depravity in predacious acts and to impute human ethics to wild predators. In following natural inclinations, predators may bear so much the imprint of man's moral imagery or motivations as to reflect little of what is natural. This is part of our conservation problem.

That there are limits to what natural areas may be

safeguarded is another part of the problem. Suburbia spreads, the roads go everywhere, chambers of commerce exult, and the catch words are progress and growth.

In attempting to safeguard what naturalness we can, we may of course find here and there—sometimes even in metropolitan areas—minor tracts very well worth preserving, along with the plant and animal life properly associated with them. These remnants of Nature can have their own pricelessness, whether they are marshes or woodlands or virgin prairies or beaches; and they can be rich in their own living forms and justly entitled to being called biological monuments or nature preserves or outdoor laboratories or given some title indicating their specialness. Certainly, let us save at least good samples of the plant and animal and soil associations that were here before the white man came. In so doing, we can insure perpetuation of some natural interrelationships to a relatively complete degree, native predators and their prey alike.

The saving of real wilderness and wilderness values can be a more difficult matter, requiring imagination, insight, and determination, together with the availability of wilderness areas for the saving and the means for doing so. A real wilderness must be spacious to accommodate the more wide-ranging of wilderness animals, notably the larger predators that are subject to such intense persecution if they straggle out of the wilderness and into settled communities where they do damage. But I believe it is a public responsibility to safeguard what we can of wilderness, before the great push of man's numbers; and to safeguard with it the wolves, now creatures essentially restricted to wildernesses, themselves the embodiment of wilderness; and the declining numbers of wolverines that also need their spacious wildernesses; and the lynxes and martens and fishers that belong in wildernesses; and the polar bears of the arctic ice fields; and the wilderness creatures that likewise belong though they are not persecuted predators: the musk oxen and the big white cranes and the shy wild ones that need man-less expanses in which to thrive.

And so, in concluding this chapter and this book, I

emphasize both the importance of regarding predation with understanding and balance, and the importance of safeguarding as much as we can of age-tested naturalness, of Life's wholeness in an increasingly man-dominated world.

Literature Cited

1. ERRINGTON, P. L. and W. J. BRECKENRIDGE. 1936. Food habits of marsh hawks in the glaciated prairie region of north-central United States. Am. Midl. Nat., 17 (5):831–48.
2. BIRD, R. D. 1929. The great horned owl in Manitoba. Can. Field Nat., 43:79–83.
3. RUDEBECK, G. 1950. The choice of prey and modes of hunting predatory birds with special reference to their selective effect. Oikos, Part I, 2 (1):63–88 and Part II, 3 (2):200–231.
4. UTTENDÖRFER, O. 1952. Neue Ergebnesse Über Die Ernährung Der Greifvögel Und Eulen. Ulmer. 230 pp.
5. HAGEN, Y. 1952. Rovfuglene Og Viltpleien. Gyldendal, Oslo. 603 pp.
6. ENGLISH, P. F. 1934. Some observations on a pair of red-tailed hawks. Wilson Bull., 46:228–35.
7. CARNIE, S. K. 1954. Food habits of nesting golden eagles in the coast ranges of California. Condor, 56 (1):3–12.
8. SPERRY, C. C. 1941. Food habits of the coyote. U.S. Dept. of Interior. Wildl. Res. Bull. 4. 70 pp.
9. MURIE, A. 1940. Ecology of the coyote in the Yellowstone. Fauna of the Natl. Parks of the U.S. Bull. No. 4. 206 pp.
10. MURIE, A. 1944. The wolves of Mount McKinley. Fauna of the Natl. Parks of the U.S. Fauna Ser. No. 5. 238 pp.
11. LATHAM, R. 1951. The ecology and economics of predator management. Penn. Game Comm. 99 pp.

12. STODDARD, H. L. 1931. The Bobwhite Quail. Charles Scribner's Sons. New York. 559 pp.
13. EINARSEN, A. S. 1945. Some factors affecting ring-necked pheasant population density. Murrelet, 26 (1):2–9; Part II, 26 (3):39–44.
14. ERRINGTON, P. L. and F. N. HAMERSTROM, JR. 1937. The evaluation of nesting losses and juvenile mortality of the ring-necked pheasant. J. Wildl. Mgt., 1 (1–2):3–20.
15. SHICK, C. 1952. A study of pheasants on the 9,000-acre prairie farm, Saginaw County, Michigan. Mich. Dept. of Cons. 134 pp.
16. STOKES, A. W. 1954. Population studies of the ring-necked pheasants on Pelee Island, Ontario. Ontario Dept. of Lands and Forests. 154 pp.
17. KING, R. T. 1937. Ruffed grouse management. J. For., 35 (6):523–32.
18. MARSHALL, W. H. 1954. Ruffed grouse and snowshoe hare populations on the Cloquet Experimental Forest, Minnesota. J. Wildl. Mgt., 18 (1):109–12.
19. ENG, R. L. and G. W. GULLION. 1962. The predation of goshawks upon ruffed grouse on the Cloquet Forest Research Center, Minnesota. Wilson Bull., 74 (3):227–42.
20. BUMP, G., R. W. DARROW, F. C. EDMINSTER, and W. F. CRISSEY. 1947. The Ruffed Grouse. N.Y. State Cons. Dept., Albany. 915 pp.
21. EDMINSTER, F. C. 1947. The Ruffed Grouse. Macmillan, New York. 385 pp.
22. HAMERSTROM, FRANCES and O. MATTSON. 1939. Food of central Wisconsin horned owls. Amer. Midl. Nat., 22:700–772.
23. WILLGOHS, J. F. 1961. The White-Tailed Eagle *Haliaëtus albicilla albicilla* (Linné) in Norway. Norwegian Universities Press, Bergen. Oslo. 212 pp.
24. IMLER, R. H. 1945. Bullsnakes and their control on a Nebraska wildlife refuge. J. Wildl. Mgt., 9:265–73.
25. KALMBACH, E. R. 1937. Crow-waterfowl relationships. Circ. U.S. Dept. Agr. 433. 36 pp.
26. CARTWRIGHT, B. W. 1944. The "crash" decline in the sharp-tailed grouse and Hungarian partridge in western Canada and the role of the predator. Trans. N. Amer. Wildl. Conf., 9:324–29.
27. HAMMOND, M. C. and G. E. MANN. 1956. Waterfowl nesting islands. J. Wildl. Mgt., 20:345–52.

28. KOSKIMIES, J. 1955. Juvenile mortality and population balance in the velvet scoter (*Melanitta fusca*) in maritime conditions. Int. Orn. Congr. XI, 1954. 476–79.

29. SOLMAN, V. E. F. 1945. The ecological relations of pike, *Esox lucius* L., and waterfowl. Ecol., 26 (2):157–70.

30. COULTER, M. W. 1957. Causes of mortality among ducks wintering on the Lower Detroit River. Ph.D. thesis, Univ. of Mich. 308 pp.

31. ROGERS, J. P. 1959. Low water and lesser scaup reproduction near Erickson, Manitoba. Trans. N. Amer. Wildl. Conf., 24:216–24.

32. PHILLIPS, J. C. 1922. A Natural History of the Ducks. I. Houghton Mifflin, Boston. 264 pp.

33. BANKO, W. E. 1960. The Trumpeter Swan. U.S. Fish and Wildl. Serv., Washington, D.C. 214 pp.

34. BELLROSE, F. C. and E. B. CHASE. 1950. Population losses in the mallard, black duck and blue-winged teal. Ill. Nat. Hist. Surv. Biol. Notes, 22:1–27.

35. ERRINGTON, P. L. and T. G. SCOTT. 1945. Reduction in productivity of muskrat pelts on an Iowa marsh through depredations of red foxes. J. of Agr. Res., 71(4):137–48.

36. ERRINGTON, P. L. 1943. An analysis of mink predation upon muskrats in north-central United States. Iowa Agr. Res. Bull. 320. 798–924.

37. GUNDERSON, H. 1944. Notes on a heavy Norway rat population. J. Mammal., 25(3):307–8.

38. CRABB, W. D. 1948. The ecology and management of the prairie spotted skunk in Iowa. Ecol. Monogr., 18:201–32.

39. DAVIS, D. E. 1953. The characteristics of rat populations. Quart. Rev. Biol., 28(4):373–401.

40. LINDSDALE, J. M. 1946. The California Ground Squirrel. Univ. of Calif. Press. 475 pp.

41. EVANS, F. C. and R. HOLDENREID. 1941. Field study of ground squirrel (*Citellus beecheyi*) in relation to sylvatic plague. Proc. Soc. for Exp. Biol. and Med., 47(1):63–4.

42. ALLEN, D. L. 1943. Michigan Fox Squirrel Management. Mich. Dept. of Cons. 404 pp.

43. McCABE, T. T. and BARBARA BLANCHARD. 1950. Three Species of *Peromyscus*. Rood Associates. 136 pp.

44. FRANK, F. 1957. The causality of microtine cycles in Germany. J. Wildl. Mgt., 21:113–21.

45. DARLING, F. F. 1937. A Herd of Red Deer. Oxford Univ. Press. 215 pp.
46. LEOPOLD, A. S. 1951. The Jawbone Deer Herd. Calif. Dept. of Nat. Res., Div. of Fish and Game. 139 pp.
47. CLARKE, C. H. D. 1940. A biological investigation of the Thelon Game Sanctuary. Natl. Mus. Can., Bull. No. 96, Biol. Ser. No. 25. 135 pp.
48. BANFIELD, A. W. F. 1954. Preliminary investigation of the barren ground caribou. Can. Wildl. Serv. Wildl. Mgt. Bull. 10A, 79 pp.; 10B, 112 pp.
49. HARPER, F. 1955. The Barren Ground Caribou of Keewātin. Univ. of Kansas Press. 163 pp.
50. LEOPOLD, A. S. and F. F. DARLING. 1953. Effects of land use on moose and caribou in Alaska. Trans. 18th N. Amer. Wildl. Conf., 553–60.
51. ERICKSON, M. M. 1938. Territory, annual cycle, and numbers in a population of wren-tits *(Chamaea fasciata).* Univ. of Calif. Pub. in Zool., 42(5):247–334.
52. SVÄRDSON, G. 1949. Competition and habitat selection in birds. Oikos, 1:157–74.
53. THOMPSON, D. H. 1941. The fish production of inland streams and lakes. Symposium on hydrobiology. Univ. of Wisc. Press., 206–17.
54. GRANGE, W. B. and W. L. McATEE. 1934. Improving the farm environment for wild life. U.S. Dept. of Agr. Farmer's Bull. No. 1719. 61 pp.
55. PEPPER, J. H. 1955. The ecological approach to management of insect populations. J. Econ. Ent., 48:451–56.
56. CRAIGHEAD, J. H. and F. C. CRAIGHEAD, JR. 1956. Hawks, Owls and Wildlife. Stackpole Co., Harrisburg, Va. and Wildl. Mgt. Inst., Washington, D.C. 443 pp.
57. CURRY-LINDAHL, K. 1961. Conservation and predation problems of birds of prey in Sweden. British Birds, 54:297–306.

References for Advanced Reading

INSOFAR AS THIS BOOK deals with predation largely as I see it from the perspective of my own experience, I believe it would be appropriate to start a list of references for advanced reading with some of my own publications.

Covering the broadest scope of anything I have written on predation is the scientific paper, "Predation and vertebrate populations," which was published in the *Quarterly Review of Biology* (Vol. 21, pp. 144–77 and 221–45, 1946). Another paper, shorter and more recent than the above, in which an attempt was also made to present some sound generalizations is "Factors limiting higher vertebrate populations" *(Science,* Vol. 124, pp. 304–7, 1956).

Then, there is "On the analysis of productivity in populations of higher vertebrates" *(Journal of Wildlife Management,* Vol. 6, pp. 165–81, 1942) which illustrates natural compensations in rates of gain and loss and especially the dangers of taking mortality of young mammals and birds too seriously. Its out-of-dateness in many ways is still not sufficient to detract overmuch from its value as a source of information, and the same can be said of "Some contributions of a fifteen-year local study of the northern bobwhite to a knowledge of population phenomena" *(Ecological Monographs,* Vol. 15, pp. 1–34, 1945).

Another out-of-date publication, though one that should still give the reader a good start on the subject matter treated, is the book-length technical bulletin, "An analysis of mink predation upon muskrats in north-central United States"

(Iowa Agricultural Experiment Station Research Bulletin 320, pp. 797–924, 1943). "The special responsiveness of minks to epizootics in muskrat populations" *(Ecological Monographs,* Vol. 24, pp. 377–93, 1954) was written to bring the Iowa findings on mink-muskrat relationships more up to date than they had been left by the 1943 bulletin.

The Iowa findings on population dynamics of the muskrat as a species were summarized earlier in the paper, "Concerning fluctuations in populations of the prolific and widely distributed muskrat" *(American Naturalist,* Vol. 85, pp. 273–92, 1951). Another paper, "Of population cycles and unknowns," *(Cold Spring Harbor Symposia on Quantitative Biology,* Vol. 22, pp. 287–300, 1957) summarized at least our Iowa findings on the "10-year cycle."

[Note: All the available data on muskrat populations are contained in *Muskrat Populations* (Iowa State University Press, 1963) published after Paul Errington's death.]

No one need go so very far into the literature on predation and populations to find himself in a specialist's literature. If I were to select a dozen or so titles for supplementary reading centered primarily on predation, I should start with Adolph Murie's "The wolves of Mount McKinley" (Fauna of the National Parks of the United States, Series No. 5, 1944); and the same author's "Ecology of the coyote in the Yellowstone" (Fauna of the National Parks of the United States, Series No. 4, 1940). Other major publications in this category would include *Hawks, Owls and Wildlife* by J. J. Craighead and F. C. Craighead, Jr. (Stackpole Company and Wildlife Management Institute, 1956); Stephen H. Richards and Ruth L. Hine's "Wisconsin fox populations" (Wisconsin Conservation Department, Technical Wildlife Bull. No. 6, 1953); Thomas G. Scott's "Comparative analysis of red fox feeding trends on two central Iowa areas" (Iowa Agricultural Experiment Station Research Bull. 353, pp. 425–87, 1947); Charles C. Sperry's "Food habits of the coyote" (U.S. Department of the Interior Wildlife Research Bulletin 4, 1941); and a paper by Edson Fichter, George Schildman, and J. Henry Sather, "Some feeding patterns of coyotes in Nebraska" *(Ecological Monographs,* Vol. 25, pp. 1–37, 1955). Two papers that are especially informative concerning hunting techniques of predatory birds are J. E. Cushing's "The relation of some observations upon predation to theories of protective coloration" *(Condor,* Vol. 41, pp. 100–111, 1939) and Gustaf Rudebeck's

"The choice of prey and modes of hunting of predatory birds with special reference to their selective effect" (*Oikos,* Vol. 2, pp. 65–88, 1950, and Vol. 3, pp. 200–231, 1951). W. Robert Eadie's paper, "The short-tailed shrew and field mouse predation" (*Journal of Mammalogy,* Vol. 25, pp. 359–64, 1944) deals with a special type of predation, that by a predator having a poisonous bite.

One of the most attractive, common-sense, readable, and reliable publications of which I know is "Red foxes of Michigan," by David A. Arnold and illustrated by Oscar Warbach (Michigan Department of Conservation, 1956). Also comparable in its own way is R. W. Eschmeyer's "Fish conservation fundamentals," (Sports Fishing Institute, Washington, D.C., 1954).

Back volumes of the *Journal of Mammalogy, Ecology, Ecological Monographs, Transactions of the North American Wildlife Conferences, Copeia, Journal of Wildlife Management,* the ornithological journals such as *Auk, Wilson Bulletin, Condor,* and *Bird Banding* contain many articles that should be important to a student of predation. Among the especially informative and readable books on natural history and conservation are Durward L. Allen's *Our Wildlife Legacy* (Funk and Wagnalls, 1954); the popular book on animal behavior, *King Solomon's Ring,* by Konrad Z. Lorenz (Crowell, 1952); F. Fraser Darling's *Pelican in the Wilderness* (Random House, 1956); A. Starker Leopold and F. Fraser Darling's *Wildlife in Alaska* (Ronald Press, 1953); and Charles Elton's *Voles, Mice, and Lemmings* (Oxford University Press, 1942).

For the reader who is interested in considering predation upon big game in relation to ecological fundamentals, I would recommend F. Fraser Darling's *A Herd of Red Deer* (Oxford University Press, 1937); Rasmussen's "Biotic communities of Kaibab Plateau, Arizona" (*Ecological Monographs,* Vol. 11, pp. 229–75, 1941); William M. Longhurst, A. Starker Leopold, and Raymond F. Dasmann's "A survey of California deer herds" (California Dept. of Fish and Game, Game Bull. No. 6, 1952); J. Dewey Soper's "History, range, and home life of the northern bison" (*Ecological Monographs,* Vol. 11, pp. 347–412, 1941); Olaus J. Murie's *The Elk of North America* (Stackpole Company and Wildlife Management Institute, 1951); Francis Harper's "The barren ground caribou of Keewātin" (University of Kansas Museum of Natural History, Miscellaneous Publication No. 6, pp. 1–164, 1955);

and *The Deer of North America*, edited by Walter P. Taylor and published by Stackpole Company and Wildlife Management Institute, 1956.

The work done on grouse by the states of Wisconsin and Michigan illustrates especially well the effects of environmental changes on the population changes of prairie chickens, sharptails, and ruffed grouse occupying a common region. I would suggest that the reader start with Wallace B. Grange's *Wisconsin Grouse Problems* (Wisconsin Conservation Department, 1948); go on to Frederick and Frances Hamerstrom and Oswald E. Mattson's "Sharptails into the shadows?" (Wisconsin Wildlife No. 1, Wisconsin Conservation Department, 1952); then to G. A. Ammann's "The prairie grouse of Michigan" (Game Division, Michigan Department of Conservation, 1957); and to F. N. Hamerstrom, Jr., Oswald E. Mattson, and Frances Hamerstrom's "A guide to prairie chicken management" (Wisconsin Conservation Department Technical Wildlife Bull. No. 15, 1957).

Finally, I would recommend Aldo Leopold's *Sand County Almanac* (Oxford University Press, 1949) for the general good of individual perspectives. There is predation in it only in places but what there is fits into a great philosophy of natural values that I do not think civilized man can afford to ignore. The predators and the prey and the places where they live are all part of the wholeness of Life.

INDEX